Other books by
the same author:

FICTION

SHADOW OF A BULL
(winner of the 1965 Newbery Medal)

KINGDOM IN A HORSE

THE HOLLYWOOD KID

A SINGLE LIGHT

TUNED OUT

DON'T PLAY DEAD BEFORE YOU HAVE TO

MARKET DAY FOR 'TI ANDRÉ

HEY, WHAT'S WRONG WITH THIS ONE?

NONFICTION

ODYSSEY OF COURAGE:
THE STORY OF ÁLVAR NÚÑEZ CABEZA DE VACA

TRANSLATION

BRIDGE TO THE OTHER SIDE

THE ROTTEN YEARS

THE ROTTEN YEARS

BY MAIA WOJCIECHOWSKA

DOUBLEDAY & COMPANY, INC., GARDEN CITY, NEW YORK

1971

68811

LIBRARY OF CONGRESS CATALOG CARD NUMBER 72–157639
COPYRIGHT © 1971 BY MAIA WOJCIECHOWSKA
ALL RIGHTS RESERVED
PRINTED IN THE UNITED STATES OF AMERICA
FIRST EDITION

Dedicated to Ramsey Clark,
Ralph Nader,
Carl Kaditus,
and
Nicholas Johnson

No army can withstand the force of an idea whose time has come.

VICTOR HUGO

Only those are fit to live who do not fear to die; and none are fit to die who have shrunk from the joy of life. Both life and death are parts of the same great adventure.

THEODORE ROOSEVELT

FOREWORD

I wrote the first draft of *The Rotten Years* during March 1970. It was a strange month, a month of open hatreds, unashamed fears, a month of sanctified insanity, of violence justified, a month when the silent majority spoke and having spoken closed many doors of the mind. It was a month of a nation treated like an ill patient in spite of his protestations of health, and the treatment was administered by many who wished the patient dead.

It was a month of murders in Vietnam and in Biafra. A month when dynamite stocks went up and accused and convicted murderers became rich.

It was a cold month of the soul and a cold month of the heart. The young and the blacks were its chief victims. Woodstock was in the past and Kent was about to happen. It was either the beginning of the end or the end of the beginning.

Only the very wise or the historians know that times like these have happened before and might happen again. Only the sinners and the saints don't worry when they do, the former because they care too little, the latter because they believe too well in the wisdom of God's design.

Five years earlier, during March 1965, in my Newbery acceptance speech, I said the following:

11

Foreword

I will write for you as if you could not get past your thirteenth birthday. And that's an important time. It is a time of finding out about what life will be like. I want to give you a glimpse of the choices you have before you, of the price that will be asked of you. And don't fool yourself, you will be asked to pay.

When you know what life has to sell, for how much, and what it can give away free, you will not live in darkness. . . . I hope that some of the light will come from my books, and that, because of this light, life will lose its power to frighten you.

While I was writing *The Rotten Years,* I often thought of this promise to my readers.

Maia Wojciechowska
Oakland, N.J.

CONTENTS

THE ROTTEN YEARS

BEFORE

By her thirteenth birthday, Denise Brown, without even realizing it, had given life up for dead. Her mind was prim and proper and totally devoid of prospects for the future. Her outward appearance was just as regrettable. She wore the plainest dresses, which always covered her knees. She combed her short brown hair severely, close to her head. She was one of those unmemorable, gray people one encounters and can't remember anything about except that they wear glasses. Although some, like Denise, don't, the impression lingers on.

Denise's mother, Mrs. Catherine Brown, brought up her only child exactly the way she herself had been brought up. She emphasized equally cleanliness, punctuality, neatness, responsibility, politeness, and keeping warm. The result for both mother and daughter was suffocation of the spirit and an air of controlled bereavement.

Mr. Brown had made only the briefest appearance in Mrs. Brown's life, and no reference was ever made to him in front of the child. He had been a "mail-order" husband, chosen by Mrs. Brown's widowed mother from the personal columns of *Bible Reader's Weekly*, the only publication the ladies subscribed to.

The Rotten Years

Matthew Brown misrepresented himself grossly in the advertisement:

> A dependable, sober gentleman, willing to make a Christian home for a properly brought up woman of independent means.

He was neither sober nor dependable, and far from being a gentleman. Matthew, from the top of his curly hair to the bottom of his tired feet, was an adventurer, if not a cad, his chief interests in life being drinking, gambling, and women, in that order. His only ambition, prior to inserting the advertisement in the magazine he picked up off a bar counter, was, as he was fond of saying, "to sail from one opportunity to the next without ever actually floundering into poverty." At fifty-two, when he bought the advertisement in the *Bible Reader's Weekly*, he was about to flounder, which led him to the contemplation of marriage as a relatively safe harbor.

A meeting at the prospective bride's house was arranged. Matthew Brown played the part of the repentant sinner with great sincerity. As mother and daughter listened attentively, he described his life as "a series of missteps leading further and further from Christian virtues imbedded in the state of matrimony." His bachelor days, he stated sadly, had been empty and shallow. Now he longed for the tranquility and decency of a home, a family, and a steady job. He subtracted ten years from his life and presented himself as a man in full possession of his potential "as breadwinner and *pater familias*." He used the Latin phrase nonchalantly, thinking at the same time of the pseudo-Latin phrase *soc et tuem*. The ladies were impressed.

Matthew Brown endured the marriage ceremony only because he concentrated on the bride's house, which was clear and free of mortgage.

When he entered it, a married man, he became panic-stricken at the thought of being a prisoner there for the rest of his life. If he had not had the foresight to provide himself with a flask of bourbon, which he downed in the bathroom, he would have bolted out the door the instant after he entered it. Fortified with bourbon, he managed to endure a turkey dinner with his bride and her mother.

The prospect of the two ladies facing him across the mahogany table, their faces so similar but for signs of age, their talk so limited to polite platitudes, filled him with sudden anger, not at them so much as at himself. What was he doing there? How could he have fallen so low, he who had dragged himself from the gutters of a hundred cities? Still in this introspective state, he found himself in the bedroom he was to occupy with his bride. Before sunrise, on the day following his wedding, Matthew Brown took a momentous step.

Out of the door of his bride's house.

Mrs. Brown discovered herself pregnant after "that night," as she referred to her brief honeymoon. She enrolled in a course in bookkeeping, which she intended to practice at home, venturing as little as possible into the hostile outside world. Before the child was born, she suffered the death of her mother, whose last sentence, uttered in a martyr's voice, eyes riveted heavenward, was:

"I brought disgrace on my only child."

As she buried her mother, Mrs. Brown promised herself silently to devote the rest of her life to bringing up her child in a protective way.

By the time Denise entered Mark Twain Junior High School, Mrs. Brown's house was the only one on the block inhabited by whites. The house was surrounded by a brick wall. All the windows, downstairs and upstairs, had been barred with iron. Neither mother nor daughter ever ventured out after dark.

As a child what Denise knew or suspected about life and people she did not learn by herself or from books, but secondhand from her mother. She knew that all men were animals and that the only safety from them was inside the house. She knew that good grades in school would denote a good mind. She knew that wearing a sweater, even in the heat of summer, was the best protection against colds. She knew that Catholics, Jews, and Negroes were "dangerous because they propagated too fast and would one day take over the world." She knew that the devil was ever busy and that foiling his attempts at perverting a Christian woman was a full-time job. She knew that America had been a great country once, before the influx of "riff-raff, and the coming to power of Democrats, Communists, and other destructive elements, who since the death of Senator Taft have taken over the land."

Through the years Mrs. Brown conditioned her daughter into absolute dependence. Constant reference to "the sacrifices I had to endure" instilled in Denise an uneasy and ever-present sense of guilt and obligation.

Before

Her mother's often repeated phrase "you are my only joy" enslaved her so completely that she never even wondered why her mother wished to exclude herself so thoroughly from finding joy in something, or someone, else.

Before she was six, Denise spent her time pleasing her mother by just staying inside the house. She had no one to play with; she had very few toys. When Denise was six, Mrs. Brown, unable to afford private school, enrolled her daughter in the nearby public school, which was overwhelmingly black. Ordering her daughter "never to talk or in any way associate with" the black children, Mrs. Brown accompanied Denise to school each day and returned for her each afternoon. Together they would make their way back home, sometimes stopping at the supermarket or, more rarely, at the public library. Once a week the two of them would walk to the cemetery to visit Mrs. Brown's parents' graves. Each Sunday they attended church services. Otherwise they stayed home.

There was no television at Mrs. Brown's house. The radio was turned on at breakfast and after dinner for news and the weather. During and after the news Mrs. Brown would feel called upon to explain to her daughter that evil in the world came from three major sources: "the devil, the liberals, and the foreign elements." At the beginning of 1970, Mrs. Brown's interpretation of domestic events underwent a subtle change. She subscribed wholeheartedly to the Vice President's view that the young, the press, and the educators were responsible for all the trouble. She only wished he were brave enough to call "a spade a spade" by placing equal blame on the

21

"colored." Her hatred of the blacks was an overwhelming fact in her life.

Each night before retiring, mother and daughter took turns reading passages from the Bible. Mrs. Brown preferred the Old Testament to the New, which she felt was badly translated, especially the passages dealing with Christ's tolerance of the frailties of human nature, and His concept of love and brotherhood.

Each morning as she prepared breakfast, Mrs. Brown would tell her daughter of the dream she had had. Her dreams varied only slightly. Mrs. Brown dreamed into the future when she would be bedridden and Denise would take over her bookkeeping chores. They would live, as they always had, in the same house. Mrs. Brown had visitors in her dreams—very often her dead mother, and sometimes the minister of her church. Sometimes her dreams included a fire that burned all the surrounding buildings to the ground. Mrs. Brown awaited impatiently this variation on her basic dream. She hoped that that part would come true and that the block would never be rebuilt. "We would have a field of flowers all around us then," she would say.

Denise considered herself her mother's friend since she had no friends her own age. She was extremely polite, neat, respectful, and responsible and did not need to be reminded to keep warm. Although Denise always got A's in all her subjects, she was not liked by any of her teachers. The general opinion of the children, who did not fraternize with her, was that she was "queer." Over the years Denise got used to overhearing unkind remarks made about her.

Before

If any people were not on speaking terms with life, it was Denise and her mother. But life, being brutally bad-mannered and insensitive to anyone's dictates, forced itself on both of them that March when Denise became fourteen.

OFF TO JAIL — Military policemen start to remove
Indians from Ft. Lawton after they moved onto the post.

Army Holds Off Indian Braves And Jane Fonda

Bill

Bid Against Bugging

Three Held, Six Sought
In Stock-Shifting Case

Prosecutor Wages War
On Official Corruption

N.Y. Bomb Terror

'Nine' Claim Credit

Judge Accused Of Bribe Loses

MARCH 1

MARCH 1

*I was too shy to ever speak to you alone. But inside my head
I talked to you often. I used to hold the longest conversations
with you. And sometimes, inside my head, I talked about you
to others. But most of all, I thought about you, trying to
figure out your essence. You often spoke of that, of the
essence of people. When I finally thought I knew what it
was I got both scared and angry. Not at you. At myself. Because I thought I could never be anything like you, that I
would die without ever knowing what it feels like to like myself. For that was your essence, you liked yourself.*

If anyone could be said to be infected with life, Elsie
Jones was such a person. Except for her eyes, large, green,
and extremely intelligent, she looked and dressed rather
like a typical old maid schoolteacher. But her appearance
was a cultivated disguise. Since people tend to judge so
often by appearances, she wanted to appear familiar, safe,
and comfortably stereotyped. But she was far from typical, and she was not an old maid. She had been married
at sixteen and widowed at eighteen. During the two
years she shared with her husband she learned nothing
of housework, cooking, or domestic responsibilities, but
much about love, joy, poverty, people, and motorcycles.
Her husband was a poet and had he lived in the Middle

Ages he would probably have been a troubadour. Restlessness was part of his nature. In the grips of the Depression he bought a secondhand motorcycle and drove it across the United States, looking for his own and his nation's soul. Having found it, he carried it around with him as if it were something to be shared, shown to as many people as possible. And his communal soul took the form of a smile.

Bruce Jones liked to begin the weekly dispensation of his smile on a Sunday morning. He would stand in front of a church, in whatever town or city he happened to be. Straddling his motorcycle he would smile at the people leaving the services. The adults' faces were always grim and disapproving. In the early thirties, although most people were extremely poor, they did not believe that anyone had the right to look dirty and strange—and they certainly did not smile back at a bearded young man who wore his hair below his shoulders. But the children loved the sight of Bruce Jones. They loved his motorcycle painted with slogans of love and hope. They loved what he wore, bits and pieces of clothes, feathers, leathers, stitched together like a king beggar's mantle. They loved his flowing blond hair, and they especially loved his smile. It was pure magic for the children of the Depression. It delivered all the unspoken promises that they dreamed of. Seeing his smile they were seeing the dark side of the moon, and they knew it to be full of light.

In the early thirties young girls were sheltered, and it was not considered polite to be polite to strangers. But Elsie was brought up by a grandfather who knew nothing about etiquette or the necessity of protecting his young granddaughter from life.

They both saw Bruce Jones as they were leaving Mass one Sunday. At the same instant they returned his smile. Taking him home for lunch, they kept him for a week, listening to him, laughing with him. He grew restless but for the first time in his life he felt that he did not want to move on alone. He asked Elsie to marry him and share his life of "wandering across the lovely face of this country." That she was sixteen and still in school did not make any difference to Elsie's grandfather. "Go with him," he advised her, "because to be with him for one day would be far better than to live with someone else for a lifetime."

Elsie Jones was fifty-four in March of 1970. Almost half a century had passed since she had had her two years with Bruce Jones, but everything she learned from him was still in her bloodstream. She learned from him about happiness, curiosity, a sense of the ridiculous. Most of all he had taught her love.

He was killed on a September night by a deer hunter. She had somehow known that her moments with him would be few and that when she lost him she would not look for nor want another man. A sadness came when he died that was to remain with her, shadowing many of her days. She had wanted a child by him and her great sadness was caused by that unfulfilled wish. She went back to school because she wanted to become a teacher and treat her students as if they were his children.

Elsie Jones was fired from eighteen schools during her

thirty years as history teacher. Whatever reasons were given for her dismissal, and they were many, some funny, some very sad, it was the very essence of her being that seemed a threat to other teachers, to the administrators, and to many parents. She had a great influence on her students, and that influence was considered dangerous by those who had none over the children.

If there was one basic belief that Elsie Jones held, it was this: Any child who is able to understand his own importance in history will grow into a worthwhile individual. She believed that a sense of history, the realization that all human beings were evolving ever closer to a godlike state, was the only necessity of life. After the assassinations of the Kennedys and Martin Luther King, she doubted her own beliefs. But when her anger and sorrow subsided, she believed even more in the coming Age of Brotherhood. And she shared her renewed belief with her students.

Because she thought that the dignity of man could no longer tolerate the perversion of truth, she wrote a history textbook with no nationalistic prejudices. She called it *Man, a History*.

Elsie Jones had many faults, and being a naïve optimist was one of them. She hoped her book would be used in schools throughout the world and that the children would learn from it that the greatest violence of all, war, could no longer be justified. She hoped that, knowing this, the future generations would refuse to ever participate in the lie that there ever could be a just cause for bloodshed.

She found no publisher. She received several polite

letters, praising her insights, honesty, and courage and expressing doubts that the educational system was quite ready for her "revolutionary approach." That word "revolutionary" hurt her more than the platitudes, for she believed that revolution never worked but evolution always did. Her book was meant to show children the difference.

On Sunday afternoon, March 1, Elsie Jones was writing a letter to still another publisher, trying to make clear why her book was a valid approach to history:

What I've tried to do is evaluate history in the light of what Cicero had considered man's most drastic mistakes:

(1) The delusion that individual advancement is made by crushing others.

(2) The tendency to worry about things that cannot be changed or corrected.

(3) Insisting that a thing is impossible because we cannot do it ourselves.

(4) Refusing to set aside trivial preferences.

(5) Neglecting development and refinement of the mind, and not acquiring the habit of reading and study.

(6) Attempting to compel others to believe and live as we do.

Those are all mistakes children are apt to commit. And those are the mistakes leaders have committed or avoided while "making history." My book attempts to make history relevant for a child trying to make it as a human being.

Having written this, Elsie Jones became terribly depressed. What was she doing? If her book was good, it should speak for itself. She should not need to sell its merits. But it was not the doubts that her book was bad or useless that depressed her. It was the fact that she was giving up on adults and placing all her hopes on the young. Did this make sense, she wondered. Was she not simply buying an idea that was currently popular?

The phone rang, and she answered it with an impatient hello.

"Hi!"

It was Mary Rice, one of the very few students Mrs. Jones had not managed to like. She had found Mary self-indulgent, shallow, and boring. During his senior year a boy whom Mrs. Jones considered the most remarkable human being she had ever taught fell in love with Mary, and now they were living together. Mary called her very often to talk about her progress in "finding herself." Mrs. Jones was afraid that once she found herself Mary would be totally disappointed.

"How is Bob?" Mrs. Jones asked.

"We're no longer together," Mary said and giggled.

"Bob Thompson was the best thing that ever happened to you."

"That's your opinion," Mary said. "Hey, I called you about something else." Mrs. Jones was tempted to say that besides Bob there was nothing in Mary's life that even remotely interested her. "How do you feel," Mary continued, "about abortion?"

"Don't you know?" Mrs. Jones asked.

"Well, I remember you saying that it was murder for the sake of convenience, but now that it's legal—"

"Bullshit!" Elsie Jones used that word when she felt something was beyond discussion.

"The thing is," Mary was saying, "I've moved in with

Allan, and we've been stoned a lot. Now the dumb thing happened—I'm pregnant."

"Oh, Mary, please have the baby!" She had never begged before so she was doing a bad job, stumbling over words, her voice shaking. She was afraid of losing this great chance that seemed like an act of God's kindness. "If you don't want it, I will bring it up. Please, Mary, I'd like to have your baby. I'll give up teaching, it will be here and it won't be a burden to you because I'll take care of it for as long as you want me to."

She waited for Mary to speak, for the verdict that could mean life or death.

"You're crazy." Mary said and giggled. "But let me think on this."

"No, don't! Say yes! Please! I'll pay all the doctor's bills and—"

"O.K. O.K. The kid's going to live." After a moment Mary added: "I don't know though if I'll let you have it. Maybe I'll keep it myself. But you can be the godmother. How does that grab you?"

Elsie was crying when she hung up the phone. She went for a long walk in the rain. How could her book, with all its lofty ideas about man as a work of God's art, make a dent in a world that legalized murder of unborn children for the sake of convenience? How could she continue teaching the young who had not been taught the basic facts: respect for life, dignity, and pride? If she had a child, she would make it so rich in inner resources that no corruption of customs, no perversion of truths, no matter how sanctified and legalized, would

33

make it doubt what was morally right and wrong. But could she do all that? And how?

She tore up the letter to the publisher and put away her book. She would cease to try to save the world and concentrate on saving a handful of children who were available to her. As preparation for one that might be entrusted to her. She sat down at her desk and wrote a letter to Harry Towns, the principal of Mark Twain Junior High School:

March 1, 1970

Dear Harry,

You are an unusual principal, and I'm an unusual teacher, and maybe we are right for these unusual times.

I want one month for an experiment with my 9 A.M. class. Will you allow me that much, without hassling me, without worrying about the reaction from other teachers and my students' parents?

For the month of March I will forget the textbook and the usual homework and work with my kids on their *inner ecology*. It's a bright class, in spite of the fact that several of my students are into hard drugs and quite a few of them come to school stoned on pot. I want to blow their minds with knowledge about themselves.

I intend to fight with them our moral depression, show them that they can shape their own future. I know there will be much flack. All I ask is one month, one class, without interference, without threats.

Oh, Harry, those same kids could become extinct on the garbage heap of our technology and greed. But they cannot die without knowing that *man must come of age by becoming a spiritual and moral being.*

Those kids must know about the nobility of their own

34

March 1

souls. I don't know why their parents have given them so very little spiritual and moral background. I don't know why their parents are only concerned about petty details and see nothing of the depth of despair or the shallowness of their children's lives.

I want to share my great respect for human life with my students. If I can make them realize how very precious a human being is, none of them will ever think otherwise.

Your resident subversive,

Elsie Jones

To Build A World Order

22 Killed As U.S. Spy Plane
Crashes Into Da Nang Hangar

Israeli Pilots Down
Four Egyptian Migs

Suppression Charged
14 My Lai Accusations

Nixon Hails Change In Foreign Aid

Internal American Troubles
Prompt Some Doubts Abroad

MARCH 2 TO 4

MARCH 2 TO 4

I was fourteen on that first day of your experiment, but if anyone was to ask me when I was born I would now say, March 2, 1970.

There was thirty-four students in Elsie Jones's 9 A.M. history class. On the morning of March 2, she told them that for a whole month, instead of their regular class, they would be part of an experiment.

"It will all depend on you," Mrs. Jones said to them. "During that month you can become potential saviors of mankind. If you're lazy, or afraid of being that important, you'll merely become better human beings than you are."

All that day they walked around in a fog of excitement and pride, saying, "Oh, wow!" to themselves and each other. That evening they tried to put their experience into words but they all failed. Either their parents were not impressed, did not like the idea that they were "fooling around," or they did not understand the great importance of what had happened, or began to happen, that morning.

"I am not sure," Mrs. Jones told them at the beginning, "where this adventure will lead. All I know is that something marvelous is going to happen. Inside our heads. We'll be tripping. All of us. We'll get high. On thoughts, on certain possibilities that are within our reach. It will be pretty heavy stuff.

"We'll be searching for truth. But maybe we'll find that truth is the only uncatchable thing in life. Maybe the only time that anyone gets hold of truth is at the very end of the ultimate trip—life. As we go tripping inside ourselves, some of us will come closer to the truth than others, but not one of us will reach it. Maybe death comes to all who find truth, and that's why people die. Or perhaps we'll discover that facts are truth.

"I hope to lead you to the starting line, where the search for truth begins. I hope to make addicts of you. Addicted for life to the search after truth. If I manage to hook you, you'll hook others. You might start an epidemic. And my life will have had meaning."

They were listening to her more intently than ever before. Some of them told her of having taken acid and smoked grass. She knew three of them were heroin addicts. None of them had ever completely trusted an adult, especially a teacher. But now she felt their trust. They gave it to her, and she accepted their gift.

There was so much that she should explain, but she did not want to bore them with why she thought this experiment so important. The main reason was that they were unlike any generation before them. For one thing, they were not "God-fearing," as their parents were. And that was marvelous, for why should they fear God? Two thousand years after Christ lived, people still acted as if He had not revolutionized man's relationship to his Creator. *Love* was the essential that He brought. And love, as little as they knew about it, was what they sang about, talked about, and hung their hopes on. Love and not fear.

"You are in your rotten years," she told them that first day, "the years that stretch endlessly between twelve and fifteen, that period between childhood and adulthood. A bird that gets tossed out of its nest for the first time is in the same predicament. But what takes an instant in a bird's life takes four years in yours. You're falling into an unknown. It's a time of panic, of great danger. You are as hapless as the bird, because there is no one to teach you to fly. You must use your own wings—your inner resources.

"Some scientists believe that we have no more than forty years until the end of man as a species. That would make you the last generation to mature before the end of the human race. In a way I too believe that the end of mankind is near. But I think man will become extinct when he becomes godlike. And therefore no longer capable of using that great cop-out: 'We're only human.'

"Almost two thousand years ago God became man and told us that we should be like Him. He preached a great revolution, a revolution based on love—of oneself and of every other human being. But revolutions, unlike evolutions, are bound to failure. You see, early Christians were the most dangerous people. They eliminated hate, fear, guilt, and material wealth from their lives. They freed themselves of all that makes man a slave. For political, social, and economic reasons they had to be killed. But not all the early Christians were killed. Those who survived began to compromise, and their children compromised some more, until Christians ceased to be dangerous.

"So Christian revolution did not work. But what is happening now? Evolution is catching up with us. Physically, scientifically, politically, and economically we've gone as far as we can. Spiritually and morally we're about to make great strides. And you are the generation who will make those strides. You are the truly dangerous generation. For now the time is perfect.

"Oh, I wish I could make you understand! Each one of you is part of a historical imperative! You must act like the first Christians and eliminate hate, fear, guilt, and material wealth from your lives. You must truly understand what Christ was all about. And that is why I believe you capable of being saviors—if not of mankind, then of Godkind. For you will be truly free of all that makes man resemble an animal."

That afternoon after school, as she made up a list of Inner Resources, Elsie Jones wondered if she had begun her experiment the best way. Did she seem to be preaching? How different it could have been had she had a child of her own. If God allowed her to have Mary's child it would be brought up realizing its own magnificence. None of her students seemed to have been brought up that way.

Perhaps she and her students were declaring war on the moral depression. And perhaps their first round of ammunition would be the explanation of inner resources.

March 2 to 4

YOUR INNER RESOURCES

	My Definition:	Dictionary Definition:
Courage:	The landscape of your soul.	"The *quality* of mind or spirit that enables one to face difficulty, danger, pain, with firmness and without fear."
Compassion:	The water you need for cultivation.	"A *feeling* of deep sympathy and sorrow for another who is stricken by suffering or misfortune, accompanied by a desire to alleviate the pain or remove its cause."
Sense of Humor:	The sun without which nothing can grow.	"The *faculty* of perceiving what is amusing or comical."
Honesty:	The seeds you plant.	"*Freedom* from deceit or fraud."
Insights:	The tractor which makes the work easy.	"The faculty of *seeing* into inner character or *underlying truth*."
Will:	The fertilizer	"The faculty of conscious and especially of deliberate *action; the power of control the mind has over its own actions*."

YOUR INNER RESOURCES

	My Definition:	Dictionary Definition:
Conscience:	That which knows the difference between fertilizer and bullshit.	"The *sense* of what is right or wrong in one's conduct or motives impelling one toward right action."
Direction:	The proper container for your crop.	"*A line of thought* or action or a tendency or inclination."

THROUGH THE CULTIVATION OF YOUR INNER RESOURCES
YOU ARE ABLE TO GIVE SHAPE TO YOUR OWN SELF

Inner Resource:	What's good for it?	What's bad for it?
Courage:	Taking risks, chances, confronting dangers of all kinds. Reading.	Concern over money. Avoiding taking risks. Playing safe.
Compassion:	Being kind, thoughtful, concerned, and *thinking* of what might hurt and how to heal what has been hurt. Reading.	Concern over money. Not thinking of another. Not caring. Being disrespectful. (There are no good reasons for denying people respect.)

44

March 2 to 4

YOUR INNER RESOURCES

	My Definition:	Dictionary Definition:
Sense of Humor:	Laughing at yourself and *with* others at their follies. Knowing the petty from the important. Reading.	Concern over money. Taking seriously what is petty or ridiculous. Being upset or defeated by silly details of everyday life.
Honesty:	Not caring how dishonest other people are. Having respect for the truth no matter how painful. Searching for truth beyond the call of duty. Reading.	Concern over money. Cluttering your mind with lies you must remember. Demeaning yourself by lying.
Will:	Trying to be the very best but knowing the limits of your strength. Trying to go beyond those limits and *not* being afraid to fail. Reading.	Concern over money. Competing when you know you can win.

YOUR INNER RESOURCES

	My Definition:	Dictionary Definition:
Conscience:	Using a built-in "crap-detector," all the time on yourself, and often on others. Reading.	Concern over money. Fooling yourself. Letting others fool you. Being easy on yourself.
Insights:	Using your imagination, your mind, and all your inner resources in your relationships with people. Knowing that you, like everybody else, is unique. Reading.	Concern over money. Being prejudiced, narrow-minded, judging by appearances. Not thinking, not allowing for weaknesses in yourself and others. Not trying to understand.
Direction:	An obligation to yourself to be as fine a person as you can be despite your advantages and disadvantages. Seeking that goal in whatever you choose to do. Reading.	Concern over money. Being discouraged because of limitations you have. Hopelessness. Comparing yourself with others and coming out second best. Trying to be like "everyone else." Giving up on yourself. Lacking respect for yourself.

March 2 to 4

The next day, as she watched her students read what she considered the most important lesson she had ever taught, she felt strangely moved by the sight of her soldiers. They seemed so very small in stature, and already so defeated in spirit at fourteen and fifteen. Were they really to be the historic front-line defense for an entire world endangered by moral death? Two students were yawning. She was afraid they might never raise arms against the injustice, having given up on themselves.

Elsie Jones had never made allowances for accidents of birth. For her a black child could not blame his color, nor a poor child his background. That life was not fair she knew long before John Kennedy had said so publicly to a young man of draft age. That man must have dignity and self-respect above all, she was taught by her young husband. That each human being started life in perfect equality with all others she was certain of.

"To change the world all you need is one generation different from the last," she began. "The thirty-four of you here in this room not only could change the world you will have to live in a changed world. Maybe you won't notice change happening, because up till now, the changes were what you learned from history books. But your generation will live in a world that will have to understand and see the changes happening. You will have to adapt yourselves, or you'll have as much trouble with your kids as your parents have with you. You must not resent change! You must not fall back on that "when I was a kid" bit of idiocy because time does not hold still, and nothing remains as it was."

"Right on!" some of her students shouted. Sometimes

her classes shouted like a congregation of Holy Rollers, for they liked to shout their agreement with her ideas.

"You ask about the establishment. Don't let anyone make you believe it's an unseen enemy. The establishment is nothing more than kids who grew up to be exactly like their parents. How does it happen? How can you stop it from happening to you?

"From the age of zero to three, without any organized help, without anybody being on a payroll to teach you anything, you made giant steps in coordinating your body with your mind. You had only to cope with a well-meaning mother, who tried desperately to make life boring for you with her cries of "*No! Don't do that! You'll get hurt!*" She tried to deny you your right to find out how marvelous, painful, and perilous a journey life is. But you didn't let her! You knew only one fact: the world was made for you. Of course you were right! But later everybody kept telling you that it isn't true. So you ceased to care, to be interested in your possession. What happened to you? How did you let yourself be conned out of owning the world?"

She smiled at them, and they smiled back. They wanted her to go on, tell them more. They did not fight it, that act of being told. They truly believed that she would succeed in making them understand on their own.

"There was lust for life in you then. You were a searcher, an explorer. You questioned everything, you took nothing for granted. You were an interested participant in the miracle that is everyday life. You were never bored because you were never passive and, more important, you were not aware of time.

"But what happened as you grew? Life began to be organized for you. By the clock. Time for nursery school, kindergarten, Cub Scouts, or dancing classes or whatever else people think up to prevent you from being bored. But you weren't bored! Not then, not while you were still living in a disorganized but highly creative way. The moment your time became rationed, time became real. And it slowed you down.

"Unwittingly, but in a highly efficient way, your parents, your teachers, nature itself, was preparing you for a great comedown of childhood: your rotten years, those dreadful years between twelve and fifteen."

There was some laughter now and a few of her students began to talk among themselves and some hands went up, but she ignored all of this and went on:

"Don't stop me now. O.K.? So what happened when you reached your rotten years? In self-defense—or was it self-attack?—you made a choice: you started to go 'steady' just to be with someone of the opposite sex who was in the same mess. Or you 'took it out' on the world by committing a crime like stealing, mugging, or vandalizing. Or you took dope or you 'figured it all out' and blamed your miserable state on your parents, or your school, your color, or lack of money, and settled into an attitude of 'what the hell's the use anyway?' toward life. Maybe you sought and found a crowd of kids your age, as confused and miserable as you, and got lost in mutual boredom. Or you pretended that nothing had changed, that everything was still fine. You began to play dead by being passive and submissive.

"Or you realize that you are going through your rotten years and decide to survive them with as much style as possible."

She stopped for breath. They waited for her to continue. She felt their warmth toward her, and they felt her warmth toward them.

"Before I cheer you up, let me tell you that when you have problems, at home and in school, or with your friends, they will seem magnified during your rotten years. For one thing, physically and emotionally you have nowhere to go. Physically you're stuck in school without the right to be a dropout, stuck at home without the guts to take your chances in the cold outside world. And besides, even guts wouldn't do you any good. Police would bring you back. You're a virtual prisoner of those in-between years. Emotionally you're not ready to take on another human being. You're far too young to get married, and it's pretty silly at your age to think of sex."

There were some outcries of protest, which she waved aside.

"Let's face it. Your sexual equipment, during your rotten years, can be compared, if you want me to be cutesy-poo, to an erector set and a pegboard. You'd know how to use it, I don't doubt, but as somebody once said, sex is too great to screw around with."

The bell rang as they were laughing.

"What have you got going for you? Where can you go when you have nowhere to go? Tune in tomorrow, same time and place, to find out. And now goodbye and thanks. You're shaping up all right."

Mrs. Jones's 9 A.M. history class was no more special than any other class she had taught. What was special was the time, that cruel month of March, 1970. There were no Juliets and no Romeos in that class, there were no geniuses and no great beauties. Not one of them really believed that he was most important to the history of mankind, that he had a vital part to play in the destiny of man. Most of them thought that the experiment was a game, more exciting than their regular class. Others believed that if they listened they would get better at what they already had learned: how to survive by protecting themselves from getting hurt in life. If they were asked if what Mrs. Jones was trying to teach them would actually make a great difference in their lives, they would probably answer no. Only Denise Brown hoped and feared that it might.

The Drift Is To The Right,
And The Temper Is Tough

Campaign

Jobs Short For Longhairs

Vote

Agnew, Mitchell
Collision Ahead?

Wallace Faces A Tough
Race For Governor

MARCH 4

MARCH 4

At first I was so pleased that my mother wanted to know everything that was said in your class. She would ask me questions far into the night, sometimes making me repeat more than twice what you had said to us. I knew from the beginning that she did not approve of you or your ideas. What I didn't notice at first was the hatred she felt for you. Maybe at first she did not hate you, only feared you. I don't know why, maybe it was your influence over me that she feared. I must have sensed it because I never told her how very much you meant to me. Should I have worried then? Should I have known that something terrible was going to happen?

That night, Denise, who hardly ever remembered any of her dreams, had a dream that she was to remember for a very long time.

She was standing on a platform when a train pulled up. She got on. She didn't know how she got there or why. A conductor came and handed her a pair of dark glasses and said:

"You must wear these glasses until the end."

"The end of what?" Denise asked.

"Why, the end of your trip, of course."

As the train began to move she turned to him and asked: "Where am I going?"

This time the conductor looked at her as if he were truly shocked by her ignorance.

"You're on your trip," he said, wrinkling his forehead as though he had forgotten something.

She was afraid to ask him any more questions, but she had to know.

"But where to?" she asked.

"Put your glasses on," he said sternly. "Didn't I tell you? You're on a trip inside yourself?" And then he left and she was alone.

She had her glasses on now and she saw nothing. She thought perhaps the train was going through a tunnel. After a while the conductor came again and she was glad because she could see him. And she felt happy because he was smiling down at her.

"Aren't those wondrous things you're seeing?" he asked and smiled back at her.

She nodded her head politely because she was afraid of telling the truth, that she saw nothing at all. And then he left and she sat alone and silent, again seeing nothing at all.

Once again the conductor came, yelling, like a regular conductor: "Station one! People!"

She was glad to be getting off the train. She was in a town where everybody was wearing dark glasses, just like the ones she had on. She tried to remove hers, but they would not come off. She felt very nervous now. People were hurrying by and they often bumped into her and into each other and nobody was apologizing. She was looking for someone she might know. Although now she could see the houses and the people, nobody seemed able to see her. She went back to the station to wait for the train.

When it came, the conductor helped her on. He was friendlier now.

"I'm so happy you want to see more of the wondrous sights we have in store for you," he said and smiled.

But exactly the same thing happened. She tried to see those sights but she saw nothing except the reflection of her own face in the window. And she grew very uncomfortable.

The train kept going; sometimes it seemed to be rising and sometimes falling. She tried to take her glasses off again, even tried to smash them, but the glasses stuck to her nose. The conductor came back and shouted:

"Station two. Problems."

This time she was happy to get off. The train pulled away, and she found herself in another town where most people wore glasses just like hers. Only the small children didn't have glasses. They acted normal but their parents treated them as though they were very bad, pushing and hitting them and yelling at them, although Denise could not see anything the little kids did wrong. She approached a little girl who had been hit by her mother and asked her to help remove her glasses.

"What glasses?" the little girl asked. She walked around Denise. "You're not wearing any."

"When Denise got back on the train, she felt different. She could see. Not outside but inside. She could see all the other passengers. There were quite a few of them, except there were no little children. Most were adults, both black and white. Some looked very rich, and some looked poor. And there were some young people. It was strange because Denise seemed to recognize a few. Before she could hello to them, the conductor was back, leaning over and saying:

"Aren't those the most wondrous things you've ever seen in your whole life?" He was speaking only to her, but the other passengers were nodding in agreement.

Nobody was talking. Denise felt very uncomfortable. She looked out the window, but once again she saw nothing, as if they were riding through a dark tunnel.

"Last stop. Self!" The conductor's voice was louder than ever.

As soon as some of the people left, they handed their glasses to the conductor. Others said they wished to keep the glasses as souvenirs.

"Good luck to you," the conductor said at the door.

"Thank you," Denise said.

"Do you want to keep your glasses?"

She held them in her hands, and he repeated the question.

"I don't know," she said. "Should I?"

"It's up to you," he said.

"What if I do?" she asked.

"You'll be sorry," he said.

"What if I don't?"

"You'll be sorry."

She got angry and handed him the glasses. Then she noticed that most of the passengers were still wearing theirs. Others were holding them and fingering them to make sure they still had them. Denise was scared because she knew she should have kept her glasses, that the conductor had somehow tricked her.

She saw a blind man leaning against a building handing something to those who had given up their glasses. She had hoped he was going to give hers back to her, but instead he handed her a piece of paper. Before she could read what was written on it, she woke up.

At breakfast Mrs. Brown told Denise that once again she had dreamed of a fire destroying the neighborhood. For a moment Denise was tempted to tell her mother about her own dream. But she was afraid that it would upset her, and she also was afraid of what her dream might mean. For she had looked for her mother in her dream. But her mother had not been there.

The God Question

Theologian Predicts Changes
In Celibacy, Divorce Policies

Separate
But Equal
Wins New
Champions

When World Fails
To Return A Smile

Crowds Relive His Dream

King Film
Tugs At Emotions

An era, a painfully re . : era, was relived in theaters · ·ugh-out the country last nigh· .

Men and women, m.·". of

'of itself as "Bull" Connor, the segregationist p o l i c e chief of Birmingham, Alabama, during the Birmingham civil r i g h t s campaign. referred t· "D.''

night as a tribute to the slain civil rights leader and as a ben-efit to raise $5 million to sup-port organizations dedicated to narr·ing on his work and teach.

poor bus service in black areas of town. It is assigning poor teachers to black schools, or it is teachers who are assigned to

MARCH 5 TO 8

MARCH 5 TO 8

Maybe if she had written you, like those other parents, maybe . . . She did not write you but she began to talk about you. She thought you were doing "the devil's work" and she wanted me to agree and "reject" you. I tried to explain you to her but it was no use. She was becoming stranger each day and you seemed to be always on her mind now. She told me that God had chosen me to expose you as an "anti-Christ," but that the time was not yet. I was beginning to worry then. But what I worried about was her forbidding me to go to school.

March 5, 1970

Dear Dr. Hutton,

I do appreciate your not minding that word "bullshit," which is in danger of becoming my favorite word. And I am glad your son Mark showed you the list of inner resources. You have a perfect right to object to what you call "certain omissions." You said you object to those omissions as a "minister as well as a parent."

I did not include *Character* because that is *the sum total,* as seen by others, of what we do (or don't do) with our inner resources. *Personality* is skin-deep and unimportant, like our appearance. Besides, it hardly ever changes after the age of five, although character does. Many great people (Beethoven, Robert Kennedy) had rotten personalities, but were men of great character. *Humility* and *modesty*, those priggy twins, don't make it on my list of inner resources because they usually tend to nag HONESTY to death. *Self-discipline* is nothing more than WILL's servant. *Responsibility* is only that which we show when we cultivate our *inner resources*. *Respect* is that which we *automatically* owe to each other. And I did not forget *Confidence*. We live in an age not fashioned for it. What we might have, however, is *hope*. But that's a gift of idealists, visionaries, poets, and madmen. Not everyone is lucky enough to come by it. And those who have the gift of hope cannot cultivate it. It's an incorrigible virtue.

I don't share your concern over Mark's apparent lack of feeling for religion. I think he is highly religious. Although he might not admit to finding God in church, he definitely is searching for his personal God in people. And after all, isn't that where Christ told us to look for Him?

Sincerely,

Elsie Jones
Mark Twain Junior High School

March 6, 1970

Dear Mrs. Price,

You said in your letter: "Everything but black studies is a waste of time for my kids as far as I am concerned." I suggest you are not concerned far enough. Your priorities are mixed up. Your children are human beings first, Americans next, and "beautiful" not because of the color of their skin but because they happen to *be*. I really do not see how you can try to make them believe that they are Africans. Their African ancestors have been quite safe in their graves for centuries. I suggest that I do not teach "white" anything and promise you that I'll resist the temptation to characterize anything as "black and white." But I hope you do not object to my fighting against making my students' existence gray.

Sincerely,

Elsie Jones,
Mark Twain Junior High School

March 7, 1970

Dear Mr. Cunningham,

I certainly will tell Charlie that you found a copy of *Playboy* under his mattress. It's unfortunate that he chose to put the explanation of inner resources inside that particular publication, which I consider more prankish than dirty. It gives many grown males a highly retarded idea of sex. And what it does for growing boys heaven only knows.

Your concern over my "discrediting" $ is probably justifiable in the light of your profession. A banker certainly would have to find another sort of employment if our capitalist system became obsolete. The fact is, however, that the system is obsolete but no one has yet found a suitable substitute.

I presume you are of the generation tainted by our economic depression. Our recovery from that disaster took a great toll on our inner resources. I do believe those resources and wants, for we want far more than we need. Or are our

As a banker you're in an enviable position. You can witness, firsthand, how those inner resources are mortgaged in the process of acquiring a house or a loan. We pay with the hides of our souls for whatever we're able to buy with $.

But what a marvelous time we're living in, for discrediting $ forever. The more we have today, the less it seems to buy. Oh, yes, we should abolish $ before it abolishes us. And how? By educating our children to distinguish between needs and wants, for we want far more than we need. Or are our young already educating us? For the youth today are dreadfully disappointing as consumers, aren't they?

You ask how we could do without $. You ask about ambition. We must become truly ambitious, to be the very best there is in us to be. And we could live without $, using human resources as currency. We could live by the golden rule. If we did, we would not allow poverty to defeat anyone's spirit because we would run the risk of our own spirit's being defeated. We could not run the risk of seeing people want for their basic needs, because we would be in danger of wanting.

It is utopia that I'm seeing? No, simply Christianity put into practice. We've come as far as we can without practicing it. For much of what glittered is no longer gold. Once I was a liberal. But liberals, like all other labeled people, have a shortcoming. They have a vested interest. They stay in business as long as there are problems to be solved. Realizing that did not take me to the dead-end ideology of the right. Communism might have been an interim solution for some countries. It no longer is. Socialism, if it is considered a steppingstone toward Christian concern for those in need, is logical; as an end-all it is not.

Finally you asked how I would describe myself. I would say that I am an optimist and a lover of man and God.

Sincerely,

Elsie Jones,
Mark Twain Junior High School

March 8, 1970

Dear Mrs. Kowal,

You say that I teach your son "useless things, things that won't help him get and hold a job." Your boy at fifty (if the scientists are wrong and he is still alive) will be living in a totally different world from the one we live in. The last frontier of man's progress is the human mind. If Tad is not prepared to use his mind, he will be a misfit in that world. All I am trying to do is reclaim his power of thinking so that he will be prepared for his future.

I know it must be hard for you and your husband to understand that all the hard work that you have known, the work that built your house and provided you with, as you say, "everything we need," does not seem enough for Tad. If you really want to understand why he resents the kind of lives you lead, you should one day visit a nursing home. Tad has. He saw people who feel themselves useless because they have nothing to do. Their lives were shaped through the belief in the "usefulness" of work. Their last years are spent doing silly little things to keep their hands busy. What a terrible tragedy that they had not given equal time, during their lives, to their minds.

Sincerely,

Elsie Jones
Mark Twain Junior High School

Elsie Jones also received a letter, that week. It was from Robert Thompson, the boy with whom Mary Rice had lived. He included an article he had written for his college newspaper on avoiding induction as a conscientious objector. After reading part of it in class, she sent it to Mary.

I think that one reason why war is a going concern is that many people are at a false peace with themselves, a kind of passive acceptance that comes from being all too aware of the failures of the past and the hypothetical catastrophe of the future.

The Rotten Years

I envision true peace as a very active thing, a very real and aggressive acceptance and coping with the moment, with all its grossness, all its beauty.

I don't expect to convert you to anything. As far as I know, that would be impossible anyway. Individual change, however small, involves the will, and a change of will can only result from a self-confrontation. You can read good words till the cows run away again, but if it doesn't happen inside your head, it doesn't happen at all.

She reread the last paragraph very slowly. Then she looked at her class. It was amazing how much more light there was now in their eyes. They now seemed committed to a fast victory.

"If we're not at peace with ourselves, we feel guilty. And guilt is one of the great evils we don't have to cope with. If there is one thing I can advise you, it is: *Don't get into a position where you have to feel guilty.*"

The rest of that morning they discussed the ways they could avoid the trap of guilt, and they understood more fully the definition of true peace.

Condemns Carswell Nomination
Goldberg: He's Unfit To Wear My Rol

70 Tenants Pledge
To Continue Strike

Envoy Kidnapers Win Terms

Woman Ruled Sane
For Murder Trial

The Public Wrings Its Hands
Waiting For Postman's Knock

Healing Art Of Saying Nothing

MARCH 9 TO 15

MARCH 9 TO 15

For a long time I did not think about my mother. Maybe I never really did think about her. Because to think about her was to see the great ocean of hatred that was in her. And to see that would be to know that she was drowning in it. When that hatred turned full force toward you, when she began to call you a devil, I did not wish to save her, I only wanted to be safe.

Elsie Jones should have been happy because her students seemed to love what she was teaching them. But they accepted too readily everything she said. They tried to memorize her words. They copied them down, shaping their own thoughts into exact replicas of hers. She was not flattered because she considered her thoughts her own. She hoped her students would enlarge and explore their new knowledge, each in his or her own unique way. So she devised a simple chart for them:

71

A WEEKLY THINKING CHART:

	Beginner	Intermediate	Advanced
MONDAY:	Play	Think	Play at thinking
TUESDAY:	Play	Think	Play at thinking
WEDNESDAY:	Think	Think	Play at thinking
THURSDAY:	Play	Think	Play at thinking
FRIDAY:	Think	Think	Play at thinking
SATURDAY:	Play	Play	Think at play
SUNDAY:	Think	Play	Think at play

Then, to make them realize that they could differ with her while respecting her opinions, she gave them the following assignment:

Grade me on the following according to your agreement or disagreement with what I am saying. (100=complete agreement, 0=complete disagreement. Be prepared for an argument in class on Friday.)

According to some scientists, we should not worry about the future since our polluted natural resources and overpopulation will deprive us of a future. As you know, in spite of our present moral depression, I remain an optimist. I believe that about the same time that you will be coming of age so will man. And your future will be shaped by these words from St. Matthew:

'Come, blessed of my Father, take posession of the kingdom prepared for you from the foundation of the world: for I was hungry and you gave me to drink; I was a stranger and you took me in; naked and you covered me; sick and you visited me; I was in prison and you came to me.' Then the just will ask him, saying: 'Lord, when did we see you hungry and feed thee; or thirsty and gave thee drink? And when did we see thee a stranger and take thee in; or naked and clothed thee? Or when did we see thee sick or in prison and come to thee?' And answering the King will say to them: 'Amen, I say to you, as you did it for one of these, the least of my brethren, you did it for me.'

In the light of these words we'll be solving all our problems:

(1) Overpopulation: not by abortions but by having fewer but more wanted children.

(2) Wars: by realizing they've become obsolete.

(3) Pollution: by seeing that earth is our contact with the heavens and that nature is a great teacher.

(4) Immorality: by using reason.

(5) Lawlessness: by obeying the two great commandments: "You shall love the Lord your God with your whole heart, and with your whole soul, and with your whole mind. And you shall love your neighbor as yourself."

(6) Violence: by understanding that it is the absence of self-love.

(7) Ignorance: by making learning a passionate necessity.

(8) Poverty: by making it nonexistent at the cost of greed and corruption.

(9) Prejudice: by knowing, by heart and with your heart, the above passage from St. Matthew.

If she had meant to teach them to disagree with her, she had failed. Each student graded her with 100 percent. On Denise Brown's paper the mark was crossed off and a large zero substituted by Mrs. Brown.

The letters from parents came again, and this time she read them to her students.

"You can take your parents' side and we can argue," she told them. But not one wanted to. She was both pleased and worried. They had to live with their parents. How could there be peace between them when the differences were so great? She despaired of those differences because they seemed to make the family a crumbling rock, and more than anything else, she knew she should try to stop it from crumbling. By now she also had developed a great faith in herself and in her students. She knew that together they could mend what was broken, heal what was wounded. Suddenly that March became a month of hope.

March 11, 1970

Dear Mrs. Peterson,

I can understand your anger perfectly well. If I were an atheist, I would be far angrier than I am. But although you can take God out of the classroom, you can't take God out of a kid's head. The history of man and of civilization is based on man's belief in, or search for, a Supreme Being, a First Cause, or at least his search for Perfection. Even you can say "thank God for that." Without that search man, with his superior brain, would have bored himself into extinction centuries ago.

It is my personal preference to knock governments rather than religions. Governments try to enslave (and often succeed—communism by decrees, capitalism by money) people's minds. Religions try (but too often fail) to free people's minds.

If you don't feel as I feel, that we are looking in the most curious places today for God, then you are not reading the daily newspapers. From such crazy attempts at salvation as witchcraft, sex, feminist movements, horoscope reading, and nuns shortening their skirts, we see a great revival in the quest for freedom and truth. If we were to unite those two needs: freedom and truth, we would get a sense of God.

Through the accident of my birth my roots were planted in the Catholic Church. But since He said: "My Father's house has many mansions," I feel my habitation is no better or no worse than any other believer's. You must feel quite homeless, and I am sorry. But you must at least believe in some profound intelligence or I'm sure a lot of what's happened could make absolutely no sense to you. I try to think of it as a syllogism.

Man was created in the image of God.
Only God is perfect.
Therefore man is Godlike but imperfect.

I became a history teacher because I see history as man's unsuccessful search for perfection. And the fact that some two thousand years ago God became man makes my syllogism shaky. There is a real possibility of success in man's search. And when man does reach perfection, my syllogism will gladly bite the dust.

My God, how dull to be an atheist! The source of all excitement for me is God's obsession with man.

I am sorry that I was the cause of discord between you and Marcia. It must be a fantastically hard chore to bring her up as an atheist. But then many Christian parents fail at their jobs too, don't they?

Sincerely,

Elsie Jones
Mark Twain Junior High School

The Rotten Years

March 12, 1970

Dear Mrs. Goldberg,

The children were given an opportunity to disagree with my "essay." Ben's grading it 100% is no indication, in my opinion, of his "abandonment of his Jewish faith."

Christians believe in another coming of the Messiah. I happen to disagree. His Second Coming (the first for you) will simply happen when man realizes that the Messiah came. And stayed.

No, I don't believe in the war between Israel and the Arab countries. The Just Cause is a lie. There never was a side that fought for the Wrong or Unjust Cause. An eye-for-an-eye justification of killing does not hold true any more since God took pity on our predicament: He taught us love and redeemed us from guilt. Ben is one of my favorite students, and I can assure you that he has been as great an influence on me as I seem to have been on him.

I believe together with all the Jews in the Messianic era, that man will yet become what God wants him to be.

Sincerely,

Elsie Jones
Mark Twain Junior High School

March 13, 1970

Dear Mrs. Dixon,

You are perfectly free to write the administration protesting what you call my "papist view of life." Even as a child I found myself in disagreement with the teachings of my church. Not the fundamental truths, but the idiocy, the mindlessness of having to memorize by heart, "the catechism." Today I understand some of its simpler logic, but at seven and nine years old I was appalled. Had I judged my faith in God by the words of many stupid priests and unkind nuns, I might be of another faith today. I am what I am today not only because of the mistakes I have committed, but also because of the mistakes I somehow avoided committing. I have a great deal of self-esteem, which I earned the hard way. Therefore, your opinion of me as teacher and human being does not coincide with my own evaluation of me.

Sincerely,

Elsie Jones
Mark Twain Junior High School

March 13, 1970

Dear Mrs. Murphy,

I don't agree when you say "Now I understand why you never joined our Rosary Society." My beliefs are profoundly Catholic, but my personality makes me a nonjoiner. I'm afraid I'd rather avoid the possibility of being bored by a group, and take my chances of being bored by an individual. I'm sure I must be missing many of life's pleasures. But I am sure the ladies of the Rosary Society miss very little by not having me around.

A member of the very large family of man,

Elsie Jones
Mark Twain Junior High School

As she read those letters, she tried to make her students understand that no one was ever completely right or completely wrong, but they protested.

"You are always right!" they cried.

She got angry with them. She never felt at ease

with the absolute trust and power they were offering her.

"Let's take the Vice President, for example," she tried again but they booed. Sometimes it was hard to control them. She had to threaten to discontinue the experiment before they quieted down. "The Vice President says many things that are right, that are almost true. However, the reaction he evokes is dangerous and he does nothing to stop it. And the reaction to his words is fear, mistrust, and hate."

At night she would often lie awake, worrying that she was not up to the chore she had set for herself. She had meant to make her students masters of their own souls and she had succeeded in creating thirty-four followers. How could she make them understand that she was only a guide, that they had to go alone to that lonely place where it is always 2 A.M.? It seemed that she had built up an avalanche that was going to come crashing down on somebody's head. And she hoped it would be her own.

Was she dangerous? she wondered. Was she leading some of those children into places where they could become lost. Should she stop? But always there was in her that great belief that she was doing good, that she had been chosen to tap what was already in her children's minds. They were thinking now, and could thinking ever be dangerous?

And always, listening to the news, reading the newspapers, she encountered the insanity of violence, the ugliness of crime, the stupidity of hate, the corruption of hypocrisy. And she thought as she lay awake in bed

about Alice going down the rabbit hole into a world
of utter nonsense. Was she going to succeed and bring
her students up from that rabbit hole? Or was she mad
and the world sane? She thought of what Mark Twain
had said about that: "When we remember we are all
mad, the mysteries disappear and life stands explained."
And she felt better.

On Sunday, March 15, Elsie Jones discovered in her
library a book she had not read. *Human Destiny* by
Lecomte du Noüy. Before she wrapped it up to send
to Mary Rice, for she thought it an ideal book to give a
pregnant woman, she copied a passage from it:

> . . . everything has taken place as if, ever since the birth of
> the original cell, Man had been *willed*; not as a superior an-
> imal capable of speaking and of using his hands, but as the
> support of the brain, the organ of conscience, of intelligence,
> the seat of human dignity, and the tool of further evolution.
> Man, with his present brain, does not represent the end of
> evolution, but only the intermediary stage between the past,
> heavily weighed down with memories of the beast, and the
> future, rich in higher promise. Such is human destiny.
>
> This Will manifests itself, therefore, through evolution,
> and its goal is the realization of a morally perfect being, com-
> pletely liberated from human passions—egotism, greed, lust
> for power—hereditary chains, and physiological bondage.
> This does not mean the definite severing of the ties between
> the flesh and the spirit, which would not make sense, as we
> cannot conceive the latter independently of the first in the
> case of man, but simply the escape from the *domination* of
> the flesh.
>
> Consequently, anything which opposes this evolution in
> the moral and spiritual realm, which tends to bring about a
> regression toward the animal, to replace man under the dic-

tature of the body is contrary to the directing Will and represents absolute Evil. On the contrary, anything which tends to make man evolve spiritually is Good.

Finding that book made Elsie happy in a number of ways. She realized that her textbook need not be published now because there already existed one book which in substance said what she had tried to say. She also realized that she need no longer be upset that no one in her class would argue with her, for she found nothing to argue about in that book. This was unusual for disagreement with other people's thoughts had always been part of her reading experience.

Just before she went to bed that Sunday, for the first time completely happy with everything that had been happening for the past two weeks, her phone rang.

"Hello."

For a moment there was no answer. Then she heard someone breathing on the other end of the line. A woman's voice unleashed a torrent of biblical-sounding curses. "Devil" and "abomination in the face of God" were two of them. As she lay awake long into the night, Mrs. Jones was afraid for that unknown woman. The great hate in the woman seemed to have been inspired by some vengeful, unforgiving God.

2,000 Seek 'A Better World'

The 'gravy train has stopped running for college seniors and many of them may be scratching for good jobs when they are graduated this spring.

H.S. Principal Quits, Will Not Explain Why

800 Students Walk Out

All-School Aid

For Mediocrity!

MARCH 16 TO 20

MARCH 16 TO 20

I was not the only one who began to notice, by the middle of that month, that the teachers were afraid of you. But their fear was not like my mother's. I couldn't understand their fear but it did not make me afraid for them. Why wouldn't they have been happy over your experiment? It made the kids tolerant and kind. It was true that they were comparing all the classes with that class of yours. In some unwanted, strange ways, the other teachers became our enemies, and we theirs.

Several attempts had been made by the teachers of Mark Twain Junior High School to abort Mrs. Jones's experiment. At first they were just uneasy about it. By the middle of March the general opinion was that pressure must be put on the principal to make her desist. But Harry Towns was not to be moved. "I gave her a month and my promise," he said whenever a teacher brought up the subject.

When, however, the teachers found out that Elsie Jones was planning to grade everyone with a B, and would not give a test nor any regular assignment for the month, they held a secret meeting. The meeting was secret because Harry Towns did not know it was taking place, nor did Elsie Jones. The students, having never been interested in what their teachers did after school, of course did not know of it.

The meeting was held on Monday night at the home of the algebra teacher, Mrs. Wesley Krummanacher, who had what she referred to as an "orgy room." It was rather a dump basement space containing a multitude of discarded chairs, an oak bar complete with a keg of beer, and a full-length, tinted photo of Mr. Wesley Krummanacher astride a definitely swaybacked horse. He was flanked on both sides by framed playgirls of the month in varying poses of abandon to their mammary endowments. The host was not present, in the flesh, during the secret meeting.

After a round of punch served with moist crackers and a dip of undetermined origin, the meeting got down to business.

"Resolved that Elsie Jones is a dangerous influence on the kids," Mrs. Krummanacher announced. "Let's hear the nays, if we've got any."

Mr. Charlton Buddy, the music and drama teacher, said nay. He was roundly booed. One by one the teachers made their resentment of Mrs. Jones known. Last September, someone reminded the assemblage, Elsie attended the meeting whose sole purpose was to co-ordinate a campaign for a raise in salaries. "As teachers we're hugely overpaid," Elsie Jones had declared; "as wreckers of minds we're hugely underpaid. What we should discuss is the possibility of a parent or a kid suing us. We have become dangerous to the children's mental health."

Another time, when a seminar was being proposed to

acquaint teachers and parents with ways to tell if children were using drugs, Elsie Jones lashed out with accusations that staggered all those present.

"I have a theory about heroin addicts. I believe they all might have something in common. I believe that they are all victims of unsuccessful abortions. I propose we try to prove or disprove this theory. For we already know that heroin addiction is a denial of life.

"And if I were a parent, I would search my conscience. Unwanted children know that they are unwanted and often turn to drugs. But why do we wonder that they want to blow their minds? Maybe smoking grass is like taking inventory, to see how much damage their brains have endured in school. For we damage them by the second grade. And how funny that we try to salvage the butchering job in adult-education classes. We speed senility along when we get hold of them again."

They tried to make her stop that time, but she succeeded, before leaving, in accusing them of wanting to become like the Gestapo.

"Do you only want to spy on them? Do you only want to frighten them? Don't any of you wonder what makes your children attracted to self-destruction? Don't any of you have love for them? Or is worry all you've become capable of?"

The meeting was in danger of departing from the immediate concern: Elsie Jones being dangerous to children.

"I think," Mr. Buddy declared, "that she is dangerous to adults but very healthy for children."

"I know for a fact," Mrs. Krummanacher said, "that

she was suspended, kicked out, or forced to resign from a dozen schools all over the country."

This announcement brought a flurry of speculations, mostly sexual. Mrs. Krummanacher, who was proud of having gotten into Elsie Jones's personal file, felt that the speculations took some of the thunder from her achievement.

Wally Rice, the gym teacher, who never failed to bring a flask of Scotch along to those meetings, now called the meeting to order.

"Will somebody explain to me exactly what Elsie Jones is doing wrong? She seems to excite the kids and that's pretty much of a miracle nowadays, outside of sports, of course."

Mr. Charlton Buddy applauded. Unfortunately this did not make Wally Rice happy since he considered Mr. Buddy effeminate.

Many alternatives were proposed, including writing a petition to the superintendent of schools, but the meeting ended in reluctant agreement that Mrs. Jones would be asked to defend her experiment during a coffee klatch the following day.

"After all," Mr. Buddy said in parting, "the experiment was to last only one month. Why don't we just play it cool until April rolls around?"

Most of the teachers agreed that that would be the wisest course, but their uneasiness about the experiment remained. It turned to anger when they discovered the next day Elsie Jones's newest atrocity.

On the day of the meeting, March 16th, Monday,

Elsie Jones's students had been given the following assignment:

"Stay away from school tomorrow. I'll make your excuses to other teachers.

"I would like you to use that day in *being alone, by yourself and thinking about yourself.* (Some of you are in the advanced stage of thinking by now.) I want Tuesday to be a truly solitary day for you, with no noise of any kind, and no activities, not even reading. If your house is not quiet, take a walk, or find somewhere where you won't be disturbed. I want you to do the following:

"(1) Take stock of what you have going for you, and where you'd like to get to in life.

"(2) Discover the pleasure of loneliness. You may, if you wish, take a break during the day and speak to anyone you choose, a stranger preferably. Ask that person a question: *"Could you tell me where I can find happiness?"* I would like a careful report on the answer you receive. Your *free day* should be more profitable than any you've had so far. Be sure you make it so."

Now each day seemed shorter than the last. Elsie Jones found by the middle of that March that she was becoming miserly with her time. No matter how she tried to conserve it, time seemed to be in possession of her. She became panic-stricken that they were accomplishing so little and that her experiment was more than half over.

Because she was trying to plan carefully what they

would discuss in class each day, she declined the collective invitation from her fellow teachers. Instead she sent them a note:

March 17, 1970

Dear Everybody,

I'm not being a snob because I can't join you at the "coffee klatch" to discuss the "dangerous precedents" I'm setting in my experimental class. You don't have to go by the book either. The times are not right for that. I shall grade my kids with the meaningless *B,* although they deserve much better because for once they are learning so much. And don't begrudge them the day they had off. It was meant to be used in the very best way. *To think.* They only have a few years to give creative thoughts to themselves. And if they don't think of themselves now, they will not be much use to anyone later on.

I've decided to use some "unorthodox" methods in that class because orthodox methods don't seem to work at the moment. Even the President (who doesn't happen to be one of my favorite people, but then neither was our last one) said the other day (March 5) that "we must stop congratulating ourselves for spending nearly as much on education as the rest of the world—$65 billion a year."

Maybe all I'm doing is not boring my kids into an early grave and keeping the educational corpse warm for a month.

Elsie Jones

On March 18, Elsie Jones's 9 A.M. class discussed teachers and school. The students agreed on the following:

(1) An awful lot of teachers should seek vocational guidance.

(2) Textbooks were written so that everything inside them seems irrelevant.

(3) Everything in school is aimed at boring the students.

(4) Money will not solve the problems, but more exciting teachers, like Mrs. Jones, would.

That day Mrs. Jones got quite angry at her class.

"You're very good at putting the blame on everything and everyone but yourselves. There is an enemy in every school. And it is the great number of you. And you don't help. You group yourselves into cliques who wear the same clothes, talk the same way, walk alike, like, dislike, act alike. You lose yourselves so willingly in crowds, assume the coloring of the person next to you. How can you be told apart, you who are afraid of being individuals? So why do you blame textbooks and teachers, who have no individuals to educate? Education is mass-produced to accommodate you. And knowledge never did, never will, come off an assembly line.

"And what of those dull teachers you have? Have you ever thought of them as insecure human beings, scared and unhappy because they know in their heart of hearts that they are dull? Have you ever thought of them as having been victims of the same process that dulls you? And when they are being taught to be teachers, they are told that you are going to be scared of being individuals. And so what happens? Things never change. No one is given courage to change. And those teachers who are different, resisting the mold of dullness, fighting against the assembly line, what of them? Do you make their lives safe? Do you tell them apart from others?

Do you care? Do you protect them from punks who disrupt their classes, who weaken them and their gifts? How many great teachers were forever lost because of you, who make policemen out of them?

"You dump all the teachers together, not wishing to see them as vulnerable human beings, as individuals, not helping them, not trying to see how much you can profit by whatever they have to give you. Because each teacher can give you something. Even the dullest of them.

"And do you fight against the textbooks? How? By forgetting everything that is in them after the tests? If you really wanted to change them for your younger brothers and sisters, you'd examine, after each year, the book that was your enemy and find out why it failed to make you learn. Soon those books would have to improve.

"But you have as little concept of the future as you have of the past. And you never raise arms against the present. You just complain. And want things without making any effort to get them. And years from now what will not be improved today will not merely remain the same, it will be hopelessly worse.

"And what will happen to you as you leave high school? Will one of you write an article or a book on the assaults on your mind? Or will you go to college, sheeplike, to endure four more years of pretense? Or perhaps you plan to become radical and burn what you were unwilling to change? What will you become? How will you ruin your professors there? For there are many great teachers in colleges today who are faced with kids with dynamite on their brains.

March 16 to 20

"I can't take sides. I can't be with you and against teachers, for my war is against injustice, not people. It is against the system that is made by cowardly students and cowardly teachers, the result of polluted lives. Children's as well as adults'."

She stopped then out of great sadness. She did not want to cry in front of them. She turned to the blackboard and wrote:

YOUR ASSIGNMENT FOR TODAY

Write an essay on *The Dream School*, first grade through high school. Make it practical, but let your imagination loose. (We probably have money to put new schemes to work, if they are intelligent.) But keep in mind that the dispensation of knowledge is to be the one and only function of a school.

The next day the best essay was read in class. It was written by Peter Baldwin, whom Mrs. Jones considered very bright. He was a poor student if grades were any indication of progress. Mrs. Jones, who had met Peter's foster parents, was sure that his inability to be an "achiever" had to do with being unloved and knowing that to his parents he meant no more than a monthly check.

MY DREAM SCHOOL
by Peter Baldwin

Dear Mrs. Jones,

You told us to "keep in mind that the dispensation of knowledge is to be the one and only function of a school." I don't agree that this should be the only function of a school today. The world is full of people who don't know how to be human beings. In my *Dream School* learning how to be a human being is very important. And my school could start next September.

It's your first day in *Dream School* P.S. 71. You're just six and you've never even been to kindergarten. You don't know what the hell is going on and you'd rather be home though home isn't so great any more. You don't even notice how attractive the school is. You'd cry if you thought it would do any good. You don't know that all the kids in that classroom feel just like you.

YOUR TEACHER: Don't be scared. I don't bite little kids. Now, I consider every one of you a little creep. Regardless of color, what church they take you to, or whether you're rich or poor, dumb or smart. You're all little creeps to me because I don't know you. Once I get to know a little about you, you might still seem like a creep to me. Or you might not. And you go right ahead and think of me as a creep. You don't know me. Part of my job is to make you understand why I am not a creep. And the other part is to find out about you. Your job is to get to know me, and to get to know yourself. Hey, you there, Come over here.

She's pointing to you! What does she want with me? you're thinking. She's smiling. She comes at you and takes your hand and drags you up to her desk and hoists you up on top of it. You've never been more scared in your life.

YOUR TEACHER: Now don't wet your pants. (*Some kids are laughing but you sure aren't since she comes awful close to knowing how you feel.*) I'm more scared of you than you're of me because I don't even know if you bite. (*Some more kids start laughing.*) Hey, you get hugged much around the house?

March 16 to 20

Did she really ask you that? She asks the same question again and then she gives you a real good hug.

YOUR TEACHER: Do you? (*She hugs you again.*) Do you get hugged at your house?

YOU: (*Shaking your head no.*) No, ma'am.

YOUR TEACHER: (*Smiles and hugs you again.*) What's your name?

You tell her your name and then she tells you hers. Her last and her first name.

YOUR TEACHER: From now on, every day I'll hug you. You might not like it but you'll get a hug from me. Now, how are you at hugging back? (*You don't answer.*) Come on, let's see. Hug me. (*She's waiting.*) If you don't hug me, how will I know how good you are at hugging? (*She turns away because you still don't answer. She looks at the other kids.*) Who else doesn't get hugged at home? (*You see several hands go up. She turns back to you again.*) See all those kids with their hands up. Who would you like to hug? You can choose just one. Your job, every day, will be to hug someone. Now, who will it be? (*You start looking at your feet.*) All right, class, we've got ourselves our first creep. Peter, you go to that side of the room and sit down. That side is reserved for creeps. O.K. next, you there . . .

You watch her all that first day. She hugs some kids; some she kisses. Those who kiss or hug her back get to choose a kid to hug or kiss for the whole next week. But some don't answer her, like you, and they come and sit on your side of the room. At the end of the week she says:

YOUR TEACHER: The first grade is for learning three things: how to be kind, how to be loving, and how to be honest. The creeps won't play any of our games. They'll just sit and think about why they want to be creeps. When they get tired of being creeps, they can move to the right side of the room.

All through first grade you learn what loving people do, what kind people say, and how honest people act. And you don't ever feel ashamed of being "good." You talk about people you know who are unkind, unloving, and dishonest, and you try to understand what makes them that way.

By the end of the first month nobody is sitting on the left side. Not even you (though you stayed longer than anyone). As time goes on, everybody goes there for doing something unloving, for saying something unkind, or for doing something dishonest. Not only in school but anywhere. You are never told what you must do to get back to the right side. You figure it out by yourself and after you've done it, you just move the hell out to the right side. Three days in a row your teacher is the only one on the left side. She said she had been nasty to her husband and can't figure out how to make it up to him. When she does, and it takes her three days, she goes back behind her desk.

On the last day of the year your teacher asks everybody what they might like to be when they grow up. Everybody says the same thing: a first-grade teacher. She tells them that they can't all make it and why.

YOUR TEACHER: First of all you've got to be real great natural huggers and kissers. Most are born that way but a few can learn. Being first-grade teacher isn't any better or worse than being something else. Maybe next year at this time you'll want to be second-grade teachers. But to be one you have to be unusually bright.

Your second-grade teacher is a genius. In only one week she makes you understand why it is important to know how to read and write. And she tells you of the pleasure you're going to find in knowing. And you learn so fast that you don't

94

even know when it happened. And then she says: "Why shouldn't you know some arithmetic? It might be fun." And it is fun because you learn math from stories that have numbers in them. By the end of second grade you read as well as most adults, and you know as much about numbers as you'll ever need to know, unless you want to be a scientist or a mathematician.

In third grade everybody gets to talk, but not all at once.

Your third-grade teacher is the greatest listener you've ever met. She only talks when she's bored—if someone is talking about dull, petty stuff. And then she says "O.K. Shut up." Nobody feels hurt because the third-grade rule is to talk about important stuff. There is some kissing and hugging and a lot of crying in the third grade because you tell each other about your problems. But there is much laughing going on, too, because you laugh at yourself and at one another. Mostly the talk is about *life* and *people* and *what's happening.* And all third graders read like mad so that they will have things to talk about. The teacher reads aloud to the class when the class is all talked out.

Your fourth-grade teacher is the Greatest Talker you've ever heard. She is so good that nobody else gets a chance to talk. You listen because that's the rule in the fourth grade. She tells you all about the exciting things she's done or heard or read.

If your family would like to know what the teacher is talking about, you get a tape recorder so that they can hear the stuff without asking you, "What did she say today?" And twice a week (and that's a rule too) you see a great movie. You're allowed to talk about that, but only outside school, unless, of course, the teacher gets hoarse or is all talked out.

In the fifth grade, you choose what you want to learn. For half the year you learn all there is to know about one subject that really interests you. And at the end of half year you can take another subject, or even two, if you want, or if you're especially bright. Your fifth-grade teacher is a sitter. She just sits there because you're learning mostly on your own, from books and tapes and films. A specialist teacher comes and talks to each kid in turn. Just the two of you. The rest of the time you've got your sitter-teacher.

In the sixth grade you learn the history of man and about people. It takes in music and art. You learn about the past for half a day, and the other half you learn about the present. You go to nursing homes to spend time with old people and to orphanages to visit little kids. And it's half and half, what you learn for your head and what you learn for your heart.

In the seventh grade, if you live in the city, you go and live in the country. If you live in the country, you get to go and live in the city. For the whole year kids exchange parents. You don't have ordinary teachers in the seventh grade. You learn from bums and actors, and farmers and architects and guys who run museums and welfare mothers and trappers and cowboys and lawyers and shopkeepers. And you learn about nature and city life and what makes people the way they are.

Then you get three months off from school to be with your family, before you go away again.

The eighth grade is the best of all, and everybody wants to flunk it, but nobody can. That's the rule. In the eighth grade you live either on ships or on trains. If you choose the train, you get to see all of the United States. If you choose to go on a boat you get to see the whole world. And the teachers are people like authors and artists, prospectors and adventurers. Every kid is waiting for eighth grade, unless he is smart and is waiting for high school.

Because high school is where you get *high* on knowledge. You really begin the study of *man*. From the beginning, when he decided to get off his four feet, or from the time he invented weapons, some 45,000 years ago. You learn about your roots, about civilization, the development of arts and religion. You learn mostly from films and hearing lectures from experts. You can't wait to hear them because they are always exciting and you have "an almost insane hunger to devour the entire body of human experience" (like Thomas Wolfe once said). And the thing is that you begin to understand how *man's search for his inner resources took him to all sorts of curious places.* And these people are very high on their own brains, and they make you high on yours. High school kids are impossible to live with because they want to live with people who are also high on their brains. So the parents of high school kids have to go to high school too, so that they too can have the same high as their kids. Those who don't get enough of that *high on knowledge* go on to colleges; those who can't stand being always *high* for four years get jobs. *But they only do work that they love.* Nobody will work just because of money, but only because of the pleasure he gets out of work. And since nobody would be working at jobs that they don't love, there would be no such thing as incompetence or somebody feeling inferior because of the work he does.

And if anybody says my *dream school* is impractical, I'll say *bullshit* and ask him why? I've already asked myself *why not?*

On Friday, March 20, Mrs. Jones felt that her soldiers had had enough basic training and were ready to go to war on behalf of their own survival and that of the rest of the world.

"A war," she told them, "has got to lead to a victory or a defeat. You end up on either the winning or the losing side, and more often than not a general can make the difference. The better the general, the more likely you'll be on the winning side.

"This will be a bloodless but dangerous war because you'll find yourself unpopular, disliked, and maybe even hated. But the time is now. Either volunteer or consider yourself drafted.

"Over the weekend and throughout next week I want you to think about your general. It has to be somebody you can hero-worship in spite of his faults. You can chose anyone, living or dead, but I don't want you to be silly and choose a movie star or a sports hero or someone who preaches violence, because those people just don't measure up. And you must find books or articles about the person you've chosen, and try to distill the essence of that person. I want you to write down the reasons for your choice. You don't have to hand anything in. It's an assignment meant only for you, for now and after our experiment is over. For the war against the rotten years and against our moral depression will continue.

"I'll give you copies of quotes I've taken from a book called *Robert Kennedy: A Memoir*, by Jack Newfield. I chose Robert Kennedy because he was a man-child of our times, a human being continually in the process of becoming. He was a man of courage in an age fashioned for the survival of the cowardly. Had he lived, I know he would have led us into a good future. But now we must go there without him."

From *Robert Kennedy: A Memoir*, by Jack Newfield

Perhaps a juvenile delinquent or a revolutionary. In answer to what he thinks he might have been had he not been born a Kennedy.

Some men see things as they are and say, why? I dream of things that never were and ask, why not? R. Kennedy quoting G. B. Shaw.

March 16 to 20

Sometimes I wish I never was born. To a friend.

My problem is that I don't have anyone to be for me what I was for my brother. To a friend, after the assassination of his brother.

It's not enough to allow dissent. We must demand it. For there is much to dissent from. After witnessing a peace demonstration.

One person can make a difference. Expressing a firm belief.

There are many who felt . . . that the torchbearer for a whole generation was gone: that an era was over before its time. . . . But I have come to understand that the hope President Kennedy kindled isn't dead, but alive. . . . The torch still burns, and because it does, there remains for all of us a chance to light up the tomorrows and brighten the future. For me, this is the challenge that makes life worthwhile. . . . At Free University of West Berlin, 1964.

I could retire and live off my father. I don't need the money or the office space. I'd like to be a good senator. I would like to serve. In answer to accusations that he was running for senator from New York only to promote his presidential aspirations.

What I remember most vividly about growing up was going to a lot of different schools, always having to make new friends, and that I was very awkward. I dropped things and fell down all the time. I had to go to the hospital a few times for stitches in my head and my leg. And I was pretty quiet most of the time. And I didn't mind being alone. Remembering his childhood.

Marrying Ethel. In answer to the question "What do you consider your major achievement?"

She [Ethel] said she wanted to have more children. . . . I think she said that. After the birth of his tenth child.

99

They will develop their own lives. . . . What is important is that they understand that they must give something to others, rather than to turn on themselves . . . Speaking about his children.

It's probably because they don't take me, or themselves, seriously. In answer to why he thinks he's more relaxed with children.

In our sleep, pain which cannot forget falls drop by drop upon the heart, until, in our despair, against our will, comes wisdom through the awful grace of God. Quoting Aeschylus to ghetto blacks mourning the assassination of Dr. Martin Luther King.

Don't ever run for President. It's very tiring. To a child running alongside his campaign train.

Living with one's passions amounts to living with one's sufferings, which are the counterpoise, the corrective, the balance and the price. When a man has learned—and not on paper—how to remain alone with his suffering, how to overcome his longing to flee, the illusion that others may share, then he has little left to learn. Quoting Camus to a friend.

Why did I lose? I didn't do well enough. The fault was me. After the defeat in the Oregon primary.

Great respect. In answer to what he feels for those draft resisters who burn their draft cards as an act of conscience.

. . . not to oppose any man but to propose new policies . . . Announcing his candidacy for the office of the President of the United States.

If any man thinks the Negro should be satisfied, let him change the color of his skin and go live in any ghetto of any of our major cities. Campaigning.

My mother told me two years ago to cut my hair. Put your signs down, I've got it cut. . . . If only you could hear the things that some say about my hair . . . no, I don't think you'd like to hear that. Campaigning.

The sisters always come out for the Democrats, but the monsignors and bishops always stay home and pray for the Republicans. Campaigning.

My small, modest, little home . . . some people might call it a log cabin . . . would you believe a log mansion? Campaigning.

America is divided. . . . The poor are invisible. . . . I say we can do better. . . . I think we need a change. . . . We must end the disgrace of the other America of suffering. . . . We have made the war in Vietnam an American war and that is not acceptable. . . . We have seen tanks patrolling American cities, and machine guns fired at American children. I don't think that is a satisfactory situation and that is why I run for the President of the United States. Campaigning.

Decency is the heart of the matter. The death and maiming of young men in the swamps of Asia is indecent . . . Campaigning.

It doesn't matter if I hurt your feelings. It doesn't matter if you hurt mine. The important thing is to get the job done. To his campaign workers.

You know something? My little girl has glasses just like yours. And I love my little girl very much. To a little girl with glasses.

Asked by David Frost on British television: "How would you like to be remembered? What would you like the first line of your obituary to say?" Robert Kennedy answered: *Something about the fact that I made some contribution to either my country, or those who were less well off. I think again back to what Camus wrote about the fact that perhaps this world is a world in which children suffer, but we can lessen the number of suffering children, and if you do not do this, then who will do this? I'd like to feel that I'd done something to lessen that suffering.*

I want to work for all the unrepresented people. I want to be their President. During the last week of his life.

I'm going to chase Hubert's ass all over the country. I'll go wherever he goes. At the Ambassador Hotel the night he was killed.

. . .

What other people have said about my general:

Charles Evers: "He said to me, don't give up. . . . He changed because he wanted to change. . . . He changed because he listened—most politicians don't listen. . . . He said what he believed. . . . He thought poverty was a cancer on this country. . . . He said, you've got to learn to care. . . . If America could only understand what we've lost. . . ."

His mother: "I shall not look upon his like again."

His brother, Edward Kennedy: "He saw suffering and tried to heal it, he saw war and tried to stop it."

On the blackboard the next day was the following assignment:

From 3:30 to 5:30 P.M. today I'd like you to be downtown *smiling at people.* You may stand on street corners, go inside supermarkets and other stores, hang around bus stops, walk the streets *smiling at people.* You should do this preferably alone, but groups of no more than three of you are permitted.

March 16 to 20

Tomorrow, Saturday, you are invited for lunch of bouillabaisse and Beethoven at my house at one o'clock. After lunch we shall write a newspaper story about your experiences downtown.

That day seemed unbearably long to the students. To shorten the hours before they could get out on the streets and smile at people, most of them read the pages of quotes from Robert Kennedy. Since quite a few of them were caught by their other teachers, resentment against Mrs. Jones and her experiment ran very high among the teachers that day.

Harbor Sewage Termed Worst

Science In The News

Deer Face Death In Everglades

Nobody
Loves An
Old House

In A Brand New Age

THE RECORD, FRIDAY, MARCH 13, 1970

Oil Slick Peril To Gulf Refuge
Disastrous, Interior Chief Says

'We Must Save Environment

MARCH 21 TO 25

*She did not let me do the assignment and she forbade me
to go to your house. I was lying to her now all the time
about you. I made her believe that I disagreed with you,
that I never answered in class except as a "God-fearing
Christian" to protest against the "evil" you were teaching us.
Those lies made her happy and had I not lied she would
not let me come to school. I wanted to choose Martin Luther
King for my general but she would not have a book about
him in the house, so I chose you. I put down all I remembered of the things you said to us, and all I knew of you.
And I hid what I wrote from her.*

On Sunday, March 22, the *Record*, a local paper, carried
the following story written the day before by Mrs. Jones's
students:

STRANGE ADULT BEHAVIOR
FOUND BY STUDENTS
IN STREET EXPERIMENT

A group of students from Mark Twain Junior High School
stood around the downtown area yesterday afternoon smiling
at passersby. The students reported the following results of
this class assignment:

One hundred percent of the people seemed worried by the
sight of smiling children. Some worried because they thought

"the kids were up to something." Others worried because they believed the kids have "already done something," and still others thought that the kids "were on something." The students deduced the following: (1) Adults worry when they see children smile for no obvious reason, and (2) People have become unused to seeing anyone smile.

As a further experiment the same thirty-three students began to apologize to people. They said "I'm sorry," to all passersby and shoppers. About 45% of those who heard them responded, "That's all right, kid"; 32% said, "Well, don't do it again"; 16% said, "You certainly should be"; 5% said, "It's about time." Only 2% made no response.

The conclusions were: (1) Adults are made happy by apologies. (2) People rarely get apologized to. When they do, they tend to become confused. (3) Adults really believe children are always guilty of something.

The experiment, which was to last for two and a half hours, was shortened by the local police, who insisted the students "move on." Their protestations that they were conducting an assignment given them by their teacher did not influence the police in any way.

In an experiment earlier last week some of the same students asked passersby

"Where can I find happiness?"

Of those queried, 80% responded, "What's that, a street or something?", 18% ignored the question, and 2% answered with a variation on: "You just be a good kid and you'll make everybody happy." The students were disappointed with those results since they expected to learn much more than they did.

After a reporter from the *Record* visited Mrs. Jones's class on Monday morning, he filed the following story:

March 21 to 25

STUDENTS CURIOUS ABOUT
THEIR FUTURE (OR LACK OF IT)
DEMAND MORE THAN ECOLOGY COURSES

A group of students from Mark Twain Junior High School, worried about the advances of technology threatening their "burial under the garbage heap of greed," have demanded that they be taught ecology courses. They wish, they said, to be informed, on a daily basis, of the latest in the dangers of pollution. Their demands have met with indifference from school authorities and the PTA, inaction from the Secretary of Health, Education, and Welfare.

"We have this great teacher," Paul Byrne, the son of Donald Byrne, leading Republican candidate for mayor, said in an interview, "we've tried everything to pressure our school but have had no luck so far. We wrote the Secretary of HEW a couple of months ago and had no answer. But we're not giving up. In the meanwhile we're learning about Bobby Kennedy and we're trying to decide what he might have done in our place."

"Are you a Democrat?" our reporter asked.

"I'm an American," he replied. "If I were old enough to vote I'd vote for the man and not the party."

"Would you vote for your father?"

"I'm not sure," he replied. "But let me tell you what we plan to do while waiting for these ecology courses in our school. First, we've begun to read the papers and we would like yours to carry more news about pollution. We have pledged ourselves to pick up all garbage we find. And there is a hell of a lot of it in our town. We are also sending patrols to see if our streams, rivers, and ponds are being polluted by industry and individuals. We intend to picket those businesses that pollute the air, land, and water. And we also intend to picket the stores that sell stuff that pollutes. You know, detergents and those new antienzymes, bottles you can't return, and all those cans and colored paper products, they're great polluters. And we're thinking of making 'citizen's arrests' on litterbugs. The thing is, we're just waking up to all kinds of stuff that is going on and we intend to stay awake, thanks to this teacher of ours, Mrs. Elsie Jones."

The *Record* was unable to interview Mrs. Jones who said as she was "too busy" to grant an interview at this time. Peter's father did not wish to discuss either his son or his son's teacher.

Our reporter was told by the principal, Mr. Harry Towns, that "some of the kids at Mark Twain Junior High are waking up. I guess they're tired of being bored." On the subject of Mrs. Jones, he said: "She's a great lady, and by her own admission, a subversive teacher. I hope she stays that way. It's fun to have her around. And we're going to have ecology courses soon.

Mrs. Jones's fellow teachers were unwilling to be quoted about the "experiment" or Mrs. Jones. One of them, who asked not to be identified, said: "I don't put much stock in troublemakers."

Mrs. Jones's small army soared ever higher and with the greatest of ease over social, economic, and political problems. Where they seemed to grind to a halt was with their home problems. Their teacher hated those petty interludes when a boy would speak about a chore demanded by his father with as much resentment as when he talked about the injustice of poverty; when a girl complained about not being allowed to go out on a date with as much passion as she reserved for the insanity of prejudice.

On Tuesday, March 24, Mrs. Jones decided to devote the class to "Surviving Your Parents."

"Don't expect anything but problems and trouble with your parents if you don't have mutual respect, trust, and understanding. What's so rotten is that you expect all three from your parents first. You've got it all wrong. You should begin to trust, to respect, and to understand your parents if you ever hope to have your parents trust, respect and understand you. If you're not going to make it with your parents, you won't make it with whomever you're going to work for or marry later in life.

"The rotten fact is that your generation has it worse than most. There are two reasons for this:

(1) Your parents have been so badly scared by the Depression that they've sacrificed even common sense on the altar of material security.

(2) Parenthood has officially been declared a chore rather than life's greatest pleasure.

"If you're really unlucky, you might be an unwanted child. But if that's the case, it might not even be your parents' fault. Maybe their marriage was going from bad to worse when some well-meaning friend suggested: "Why don't you have a kid?" And they followed the advice. You might have saved the marriage or you might not have, but that's not your problem. Your parents might not have planned on having you, but that's not your problem either. Your problem is finding a solution to surviving the close proximity of people with problems. And all parents are beset by problems. Loving your parents, for no other reason than that they are fellow human beings first and your parents second, will make the job easy. And more than that, you simply must understand that you cannot change their personalities. Problems are always the result of the clash of personalities and the clash of wills. You must learn to live with their personalities because they're the only ones they've got.

And their will has to have priority over yours, no matter how insane their demands; in your rotten years you've got to obey. That's another reason they are rotten years.

"So let's examine all the moaning, the nagging, all the hassle. On both sides. Yours and your parents."

She turned to the blackboard, where she had written earlier that morning:

WHAT YOU WANT	WHAT YOUR PARENTS WANT
To be left alone. Not to be perpetually nagged, put down, criticized, made to do chores you don't feel like doing.	To be respected by you. Not to be perpetually disobeyed, put down, criticized, made to do what you should do. Not to be worried.

"On closer examination it seems that you and your parents actually want essentially the same things. Except for 'worrying'—and let's get rid of this right here: it comes with the territory of being a parent, so nobody should try to eliminate worrying; it's just a natural cross a parent has to bear. You could compromise and make an almost equal exchange. "I'll do this and you'll do that" should put an end to much unhappiness between you and your parents. It's easier said than done, right? But why?

"Partially because you have so little understanding of each other. The lack of understanding is rather puzzling when you consider your parents. They have at least three advantages:

(1) They were once your age themselves (and you were never theirs, and that is the *cause* of their worries).

(2) They have hundreds of books which explain *you*

to them, while you have none about them that I'm aware of, except for the entire body of literature, if only you took the trouble to read!

(3) They see you pretty much as you are, while you don't see them as human beings, individuals, but only as your parents.

"At the risk of sounding unsympathetic, let me say that I think that problems between kids and their parents are not only *catastrophically boring* but fairly simple to solve. The fastest beginning would be if only you could *hear* (without being seen) what your parents say about you to other parents. If you think they have no sense of humor, you would probably discover that indeed they do. But simple solutions always seem to have some catch to them. How can anyone be invisible? (They can't but you can at least be understanding, by using your *inner resource* of INSIGHT.) Let's try to understand the limitations of being a parent and a child."

She pointed to the blackboard again.

LIMITATIONS OF BEING A PARENT

Your Mother's	Your Father's
From her own mother she (somehow) got the idea that if she didn't nag she would seem not to care (every mother today has got to be a "Jewish mother" or has to be rich enough to afford an analyst). From everything she hears and reads and sees about today's world she gets the paranoid idea that you are threatened with a fate worse than death by just being your age.	From his father (somehow) he got the idea that discipline will solve everything. But nobody today believes in discipline. He is being told that "being a pal" to his kids can accomplish the same thing. Up to a certain age being a pal worked out all right, but then you and your father stopped being pals. (You reached your rotten years). It happened at the exact same time that you got too big to spank.

The Rotten Years

YOUR OWN LIMITATIONS

None that you can see. Your parents must have changed a hell of a lot, because, not so long ago, they were really nice. They hassled you once in a while, but not all the time, like now.

CHANGES THAT OCCURRED IN YOUR PARENTS

None.

BUT EVERYBODY BELIEVES THAT SOMEBODY HAS CHANGED

Now she passed around some mimeographed papers. While she was mimeographing them, one of the teachers passed a note to her that said: "There have been complaints about your overuse of this machine." She had smiled at the woman, whose name she could not remember, but the woman did not return the smile.

"Don't read this now," Mrs. Jones said. "Take it home and show it to your parents if you wish. I want to get on. The most important thing to remember, throughout your rotten years, is the absolute fact that there is a natural love between parent and child. It's simply there and has nothing to do with how you get along with your parents. It was placed there by God. You or your parents can't destroy it. It's there to stay."

But what of those foster kids, she thought, what of them? Who had natural love for them?

"Those of you," she said, "who are foster kids and don't feel loved, you'll just have to make it up by loving your own kids twice as much. Loving or being loved gives the same kind of pleasure. And for whatever it's worth, up till then don't doubt that God has reserved His special love for you."

It was not enough, she knew. The deep hurt was in them, and they would have to fight it, or else that hurt might take over and darken their lives. If only she had the means of adopting those few she knew were being denied their right to be loved!

The bell rang then and she watched them file out of the room, those foster children she cared more for than for any other. They all had had a father once and his name was Martin Luther King. Now he was dead, and they were orphans. Will those kids, she wondered, ever forgive, or will they be bought by those who teach to hate?

That evening none of the foster children shared with their foster parents what they had been handed by Mrs. Jones. But they all read those pages. Some of them cried that night, for those pages were not meant for them.

THE WAY YOUR PARENTS REMEMBER YOU BEFORE YOU WERE 12:	THE FACTS (AS YOU SEE THEM)
Respectful:	You didn't even *know* you were.
Polite:	You always said "hi" to them, but that was when they were "nice."
Obedient:	You didn't even know there was anything worth watching on TV past 9 P.M. except on Friday and Saturday nights.
Helpful:	You didn't even realize that washing dishes was *her* job or that it doesn't hurt the car to be dirty or the lawn to grow long.
Loving:	Sure, when they were "nice" you didn't mind kissing them once in a while or being hugged by them.

The Rotten Years

Safe:

Nobody even asked you out on a date, and drugs weren't sold around grammar school then.

Good:

What was there to be all that bad about? Besides, you hardly ever went out of the house.

Responsible:

The older you get the clearer it becomes that your parents consider you a free labor force around.

Confiding:

You were too small to beat up on the kids who were beating you up so you tattletaled. You can get killed for ratting now, and besides, how would they understand anything you might like to confide in them when they don't even understand about your clothes or your music or your hair?

Sweet:

You were trying to con them into getting you things. Now you feel you have a *right* to things you need. Besides, if you could leave school and work, you wouldn't ask them for a dime.

Cooperative:

You didn't even know that you could refuse to do all that stuff they asked you to do. Besides, most of the time you didn't mind because there was nothing else to do.

Studious:

You still had great illusions that you could actually learn something in school. But the stuff they teach you now—who needs to learn things you'll never use?

116

March 21 to 25

THE WAY YOU REMEMBER
     YOUR PARENTS   THE FACTS
  BEFORE YOU WERE 12: (AS YOUR PARENTS SEE THEM)

Understanding: They didn't listen to you all that much. They were thinking about something else and nodding their heads. You bored them a lot so they didn't pay much attention to what you said.

Trusting: In those days they only worried that you might catch a cold or cross against a light or back-talk to a teacher. Since then the world has changed. There are rapists running loose and guys hanging around your school ready to stick a hypo needle in your arm and get you addicted. And how about *Lolita* and *Candy* and all the other filth? The world is filled with danger, and you probably have already had sex (you didn't even go out yet on your first date), and your eyes look strange, and who are those friends you're hanging around—are they sex maniacs or addicts or what?

Undemanding: If only you did some work around the house, they would know you are not exposed to perpetual danger. And what can happen to you if you're in bed and asleep by ten?

Respectful: They didn't search your room because you didn't have *Playboy* under your bed, and your breasts did not begin to grow and with the pill and the drugs and all that's going on how can they trust you and not worry? And

117

The Rotten Years

besides, if you can be so rotten to them who love you, how rotten are you to others, who don't? Maybe you are already hooked on drugs and that's why you're so rotten to them. Or maybe you're getting some girl in trouble (if you're a boy) or doing something you don't even know you're doing (if you're a girl). Besides, if they don't ask you questions how will they know what you were up to, and how could you stay a good child in a rotten world, especially with your rotten friends? And if they seem not to trust you, how would you know that they still care for you since all lines of communication are down?

Intelligent: They don't like to discuss big topics with you because they are afraid that in your school you're learning so much more than they've been able to learn. You're an "intellectual" to them now, with all those well-paid teachers teaching you stuff that they couldn't understand if they tried, what with the job and all the other worries to worry about.

Worrying is an occupational hazard of being a parent.

I don't know how good your parents are at worrying but most parents I know are artists at that. I know some who have actually *organized* their worries and worry in alphabetical order (Alcohol being first and Zinnias being last in their list of

118

worries). But most parents worry in a highly disorganized way and worry because they are worrying in a disorganized way because they might miss something to worry about. It's enough to drive some out of their minds. But whether your parents are professional or amateur worriers doesn't mean that you should interfere with their hobby. Don't worry about them worrying. (You're a rank beginner at worrying. Clothes and school don't even provide a real good worry. And dates or lack of them shouldn't even be considered in the same breath as worries your parents have, especially today.)

There are probably over a million people in the United States today who make good money providing your parents with things to worry about. Let's take sex. Your parents naturally worry about that. I mean, they were your age, and *that* they can remember, especially fathers, and that (remembering) really worries them. Then they're worried about how much or how little they've told you and whether they've told you about sex at the proper time, or too early or too late. They worry about whether what they told you about sex is the same stuff that you've heard about sex. (In here they can stay worried for a long time, worrying about what your friends tell you and what your sex education is all about.) Then they go to a PTA meeting and hear someone speak on the subject of "How to Deal with Your Child's Curiosity About Sex." And they worry about:

(a) What they've heard, and
(b) Whether the speaker had ever had any sex,
    (1) And if he had not whether to believe what they heard, or
    (2) If he had how come they didn't understand what he said.

The Rotten Years

And that's just for amateur worriers. The professional worrier can worry for a whole month about the variations on the above. Or they might pick up a book: *What Should I Tell My Child About Sex?* (or any thousands of similar books). And they worry because:

(a) They discover they did it all wrong,
(b) They discover they didn't know as much as they thought they did about sex,
(c) They discover they're worrying too much about sex.

And usually they do. And having left sex unworried worries them. Maybe one day they'll all join an organization PHEW (Parents Have Enough Worries) and stop worrying about their kids and concentrate on the important subjects such as:

How long will I have to stay in jail if they question my tax return?

If I give up smoking, will it make me a nervous wreck and will it cost more to be in a nuthouse than simply to die of cancer?

Will anyone be foolish enough to buy this house now that it's a wreck? etc., etc.

There is a good book that you might want to get them, *How to Make Yourself Miserable* by Dan Greenburg, which is mostly about how to worry all the time and like it. Or if it bothers you to have them worry, you might like to get them *The Peter Principle* by Dr. Laurence J. Peter and Raymond Hull, which is subtitled *Why Things Always Go Wrong* and why you can't do a thing about that.

But, if I were you, I'd just leave them to their hobby.

March 21 to 25

FAMILY ASSIGNMENT: SURVIVING, TOGETHER, THE ROTTEN YEARS

Resolved: Parents are *people* with many of the same problems we have. One of life's greatest pleasures is being a parent of a loved child, only surpassed by being a loved child. A family is a microcosm of society, reflecting most of society's problems. It should not be a *chore* to survive one's children nor one's parents. But when it becomes a problem, it's worth solving.

TEST FOR KIDS:

Try to figure out which *inner resources* (if any) you have cultivated when last confronted with a problem having to do with your parents? (Check one or more, if none, explain why.)

COURAGE___; COMPASSION___; SENSE OF HUMOR___;
HONESTY___; INSIGHTS___; WILL___; CONSCIENCE___;
DIRECTION___
NONE:___WHY?_____

The opposites of these eight *inner resources* are:

COWARDICE___; INDIFFERENCE___; DESPAIR___; LYING___;
BLINDNESS___; STUPIDITY___; BULLSHITTING___; ANGER___

Have you cultivated any of the above with your parents? Why?_____

Just suppose you have a *sick* need to be yelled at. Have you done anything to get well? YES___NO___

If the answer is NO, choose the appropriate answer:

(1) If I'm not being yelled at my parents won't know I exist___
(2) If I'm not being yelled at I'll know they don't care what I do___

(1) they will, and (2) they do. Explain in any other reason for your sick need._____

Take a guess at what *provokes* your parents most into nagging you. (Check one or more, use self-crap-detector)

(1) You hardly ever listen to what they're saying___
(2) You hardly ever do what they want you to___
(3) You never show them respect (it's not like money, it doesn't have to be earned)___
(4) You have lied to them and they can't trust you now___
(5) Other_____

121

The Rotten Years

If there is a pattern to the nagging (see your parents' test) can you break it by

    (1) Giving them a bad time right back?

    (2) Continuing to let them "take it out" on you?

    (3) "Screwing" their chances at being nasty to you by being *especially* great at that particular time, or changing slightly the pattern of your habits (watch TV at some other time, go out on other than Friday nights, do the dishes before you're told to do them, etc.)?

You may choose only one answer___

SOLUTION TO A PROBLEM:

You receive orders to improve relationship with your parents. Your survival depends on it. Your strategy: using INSIGHTS and DIRECTION.

Draw up a list entitled: *When I Grow Up and Get To Be A Parent This Is What I Will and Won't Do.* (keep a copy for future reference.) Plant the list so that your parents can find it.

If conditions do not improve, make another list and be sure your parents find it: *Places I Could Go To When I Leave Home Next Week.*

If conditions do not improve, choose a place from the list and go. (But expecting perfection would be stupid. Nothing is instantly solved, and nothing is ever perfect. Nobody is totally happy with his parents or his children. But there is *a natural love between parents and children* and it is often abused or forgotten.)

TEST FOR PARENTS ONLY

Try to figure out which *inner resources* (if any) you have cultivated when last confronted with a problem having to do with your child. (Check one or more, if none, explain why.)

    COURAGE___; COMPASSION___; SENSE OF HUMOR___;
    HONESTY___; INSIGHTS___; WILL___; CONSCIENCE___;
    DIRECTION___
    NONE:___Why?_____

March 21 to 25

The opposites of these eight *inner resources* are:

    COWARDICE___; INDIFFERENCE___; DESPAIR___; LYING___;
    BLINDNESS___; STUPIDITY___; BULLSHITTING___; ANGER___

Have you cultivated any of the above with your children (child)?
    Why?_____

Just supposing you have a *sick* need of your child noticing you, so you
yell at your child, often. Would it help you if your child:

    (1) Ignored your need?
    (2) Did not get involved in your sickness but cultivated
    compassion toward you?
    (3) Would make it plain to you that the child knows your
    need is *sick* and can't do anything for you, but you can work
    things out for yourself?
    (*All three are correct.*)

Suppose your need to be noticed by your child is *not* sick. Would you
be happy if your child:

    (1) Talked to you sometimes as if you were a human being
    rather than just a parent?
    (2) Criticized you often so you'd know what mistakes you're
    making?
    (3) Told you that sick or not your need is of no interest to
    him?
    (*Choose one___*)

Suppose you have a real rotten job, besides all the other problems of
being a father. You don't leave your rotten job because of one or all
of the following:

    (1) You'd lose all your benefits (pension, seniority).
    (2) Everyone wants something from you and you need the
    money you're making at your rotten job.
    (3) You're afraid that if you left it you would not find another.
    (4) You gave up, long ago, any idea that you could like
    what you do.
    (5) You consider yourself "lucky" to have your rotten job.

Your children (and your wife) could help you with only ONE reason
why you can't leave your job. *Which* one is *it*—Would cultivating your
inner resources make you leave your job, or stick with it? LEAVE___;
STAY___; BOTH___

The Rotten Years

Try to determine if there is a pattern to your nagging your child. Do you do most of it:

mornings____
right after the child comes home from school____
evenings____(while he watches TV____or while you watch TV____)
before he goes out____before you go out____
when he returns____when you return____
Friday nights____
weekend during the day____
weekend nights____
when he refuses to help with housework____
   "   "   "   "   "   "   chores—
Other_____

(You may choose only one answer.)

Try to determine one reason for most of your difficulties with your child._____Is there anything you and your child can do to eliminate this one reason._____

SOLUTION TO A PROBLEM:

You receive orders: Improve relationship with your child. Your and his survival depends on it. Use insights and direction:

Draw up a list entitled When I Was a Child I Had No Problems with My Parents Because. (Use self-crap-detector on faulty memories.)

Plant the list in your child's room, make your child keep it for future reference (when he's a parent). (If you had troubles with your parents as a child, make a list: It's Difficult to Be Married Because, plant list in child's room, so that your difficulties could be blamed on your marriage, not on your child.)

If difficulties with your child persist draw up a list entitled What I Could Do with My Kid When I No Longer Want Him Around The House, (listing agencies such as orphanages, etc.) and leave the list in your child's room. Or, draw up a list: Where I Could Go Next Week When I Leave Home and leave in your child's room. If difficulties persist, act. (But don't expect perfection. Whether you had wanted your child or not, whether you are neurotic or not, remember that the natural love is there. It was placed there by God. Only people under analysis deny its existence, but then they have trouble believing in God. And if you've

March 21 to 25

been "trying to get along" as best as you know how, it's probably because you've only tried in exactly the same way, change tactics, so you won't be colliding against the same wall all the time.)

RECOMMENDED READING ALOUD FOR THE WHOLE FAMILY
(*especially if most problems in family are due to money, lack of its appreciation by the child*):

"Let us be clear at the outset that we will find neither national purpose nor personal satisfaction in a mere continuation of economic progress, in an endless amassing of worldly goods. We cannot measure national spirit by the Dow-Jones Average, nor national achievement by the gross national product. For the gross national product includes air pollution and advertising for cigarettes, and ambulances to clear our highways of carnage. It counts special locks for our doors, and jails for the people who break them. The gross national product includes the destruction of the redwoods, and the death of Lake Superior. It grows with the production of napalm and missiles and nuclear warheads, and it even includes research on the improved dissemination of bubonic plague. The gross national product swells with equipment for the police to put down riots in our cities, and though it is not diminished by the damage these riots do, still it goes up as slums are rebuilt on their ashes. It includes Whitman's rifle and Speck's knife, and the broadcasting of television programs which glorify violence to sell goods to our children.

And if the gross national product includes all this, there is much that it does not encompass. It does not allow for the health of our families, the quality of their education or the joy of their play. It is indifferent to the decency of our factories and the safety of our streets. It does not include the beauty of our poetry or the strength of our marriages, the intelligence of our public debate or the integrity of our public officials. It allows neither for justice in our courts, nor for justness in our dealings with each other. The gross national product measures neither our compassion nor our devotion to country. It measures everything, in short, except that which makes life worthwhile; and it can tell us everything about America—except whether we are proud to be Americans."

(*R. Kennedy, May 5, 1967, Detroit*)

Birth Pill
Will Carry
Risk Label

Liberal Jersey Abortion Law
Wins Health Chief's Support

Legal Or Illegal Abortion
Just Matter Of Geography

Search Continuing
For A Teen Center

MARCH 26

MARCH 26

It was past midnight. I woke up to the sound of her voice. It was terribly loud in the stillness of the night. At first I thought she was having a nightmare but she was not in her room. She was on the phone in the kitchen. She didn't notice me and I stood for a long time looking at her face twisted by hate, listening to the curses she shouted at you. I knew it was you. Should I have gotten help then? Why did I do nothing? Why did I go to my room and make myself believe it was a nightmare?

Elsie Jones meant to have her phone disconnected or her number changed but each time she thought of it it was too late, the business office of the phone company was closed for the day. She tried, each time the woman called, to reason with her, to make her understand that she was ill and should have help. She did not want to think of who it might be. What mother of which child. She just hoped the calls would stop.

Before it came that night she had written a letter to the chief of police.

March 25, 1970

Dear Chief Woods:

You must grant us a police permit for our *Love Thy Neighbor Parade* on Easter Sunday!

I wouldn't want to bribe you, but I'd like to make a

deal. I understand you are to give a speech to the Tri-State Commission on Narcotics tomorrow night. I enclose a paper written by a few of my students, who have spent some time talking to kids about their use of drugs. It goes to you with their compliments; use it as your own if you wish. You see it is so important to have that Easter Parade. We even have a sign for you or any policeman who wants to participate: *"If Christ Was Alive Today He Would Be A Cop. Would You Call Him a Pig?"* We've got other signs all ready: *"Christ Wore Long Hair and He Would Wear It Long Today,"* which will be carried by a long-haired boy. And *"When I Was Hungry You Fed Me,"* which was made by a welfare mother, and a priest will carry one saying: *"His Last Law Was: Love One Another."* And an ex-con, who happens to think well of you by the way, will march with us holding a sign reading: *"When I Was In Prison You Visited Me."* and a bum: *"When I Was Naked You Clothed Me."* And a bunch of nuns have promised to join us and chant the Beatitudes. It will be the greatest Easter Parade ever, and we have a right to it. We don't want to get bogged down in red tape because that would be too hard to explain to the *Record*.

Best,

Elsie Jones
Mark Twain Junior High School

P.S. Next Monday I plan to hitchhike. I'll be on the corner of Valley Road and Minnehaha Boulevard at 4 P.M. Could you arrange to have one of your men give me a summons. I need it because I plan to fight through the courts the law that prohibits hitchhiking. E.J.

As she finished the letter, the phone rang. It was too early for her usual caller, who never called before midnight.

"Hi. It's Mary." She was not giggling. "I've got something to confess to you." And then another voice. "This is Bob Thompson. She told you it wasn't my kid. Well, it is. And I want to thank you for having wanted to keep it for us but now we're back together again. . . ." Again the phone changed hands. "Guess what?" Mary asked. "We're going to get married. Not now. Not until I start having labor pains. I want to marry him then. While in labor. Isn't that crazy?"

It was not to be after all. The things she had bought, the clothes, the diapers and bottles, a folding bassinette, a high chair, an antique crib fit for a prince. . . . Those would not be used in her house. And she would never know how it is to have a baby around. Her tears were not noble. They were not for the baby or Bob and Mary. They were for her own immeasurable loss.

Later that night she began to think that maybe she could adopt one of the children in her class, one of the foster kids. Peter Baldwin, perhaps. Or maybe the lot of them. And then the phone rang, and she knew who it was.

Usually she went to sleep quite soon after listening to the woman but that night she lay awake a long time. She couldn't forget the threats against her life or her plans for adopting some foster kids from her class. That night she knew the threats were more real than her plans. She reached for a book and before falling asleep read these words:

> I don't know what will happen now. We have got difficult days ahead, but it doesn't matter with me because I've been to the mountaintop. Like anybody else I would like to live a long life. But I'm not concerned with that. I just want to do

God's will and he has allowed me to go up the mountain. I see the promised land. I may not get there with you, but I want you to know tonight that we as a people will get to the promised land. I am happy tonight that I am not worried about anything. I'm not fearing any man. Mine eyes have seen the glory of the coming of the Lord.

Status Quo Asked On Marijuana Laws

Addicts' Parents Angry

Drug March Planned On Capitol

Chief Backs Teen Harassment

Scouts Warned
Of The Danger
In Marijuana

Making Very Little Headway

Below The Surface Of The News

Punitive Pot Laws Are Restudied

Narcotics
—Who's
At Fault?

By the time you see the drowsiness and the runny nose your child has had it," he said. "It's too late then. About the only thing you can do is take them to a hospital to have them detoxified so they don't have to go through the agony of withdrawal.

He said 80 per cent of felony cases that come before the Public Defender's Office were drug cases or cases involving drugs, such as burglaries committed to finance a drug habit.

Two Towns To Act
War On Drugs Growing Wider

MARCH 27

MARCH 27

I had been thinking all week how I would tell her about the parade. I was going to make my stand on that. She was not going to prevent me from going. She let me talk about it, not interrupting, not asking questions, just listening. I thought that she approved, finally, of something that you were doing. I thought a miracle had happened and that she had changed. Later that day, she asked me if I wanted to take a walk with her. She wanted to see where you live. And I hoped that we would go inside your house, that she would want to see you and tell you that the parade was a marvelous idea. I hoped she would want to apologize to you for that call. But she only wanted to see where you live. You never noticed us, you were at your desk writing. And then, without a word, she turned back and it was a cold evening. And it was a dark night. There was no arguing with her. She was quite mad. She thought that you had stolen me away from her. And it was Good Friday, after dark, and He was dead.

Mrs. Jones's experiment was over before she realized it. She had given her word that on April 1 she would resume her regular history class at 9 A.M. There was too much left unsaid. Time had been her enemy but she was going to cheat time. She was going to write down certain thoughts, directions, and assignments. She would mail them to Harry Towns and ask his permission to mimeograph her "final attack." Then she would rest.

She spent that afternoon at her desk, writing.

At this point we must all keep asking ourselves: "Am I part of the solution, or part of the problem?" You've made me think I might be part of the solution. Your parents and other teachers have made me feel that I might be part of the problem. God only knows who's right. I find myself, as I grow older, agreeing about 30 per cent of the time with people I usually disagree with, and disagreeing 30 per cent of the time with people I generally agree with. And that's sort of wise, because nobody is totally right or totally wrong.

I haven't taught conventional history this month and yet everything we talked about will become history because our lives are what make history. What happens when things go right is that people adjust to their time. When things go wrong people try to adjust the time to themselves. We're in a technological age and are not adjusting well because we consider the world dehumanizing. Well, is it?

We live in a society that is *sponsoring* the following events (and you are being asked by the sponsors to participate):

Organized alienation (between parents and children)
Overkill of sex (in books, movies, theaters, etc.)
Unhurting pain (through pills, liquor, and drugs)
Sanctification of mediocrity (on television)
Cultivation of feeblemindedness (in school)
Belief in money as detergent of wrongs (by government)
Desire for more money as it buys less (by everyone with a job)
More sincerity in "honest" lying (by organized religions)
Endorsement of violence, that private insanity gone public (by the Black Panthers, the Weathermen, and other radical groups)

March 27

At the same time, the same society has the following *unsponsored* events:

> Laughing
> Making mistakes and learning from them
> Having fun
> Exploring what all the madness is about
> Pursuit of happiness
> Fighting against moral depression
> Acceptance of pain
> Making an art of crap-detecting (with patent pending in your name for a crap-detector)

It's up to you which events you want to choose, the sponsored ones, or the unsponsored ones.

Just in case you don't know how a *crap-detector* works, let's pretend you overhear the following: (which I did):

Gary: I went out with Peggy Pierce last night. (*He rolls his eyes suggestively.*)

Joe: Oh, yeah? Peggy Pierce? I heard she's entering a convent.

Gary: She sure didn't act like it last night. (*Rolls his eyes some more.*)

Joe: Who you kidding? Peggy Pierce wouldn't let anyone touch her, not even her idol, Mick Jagger. I could just hear her: "Oh, Mick, stop it! I'm not that kind of girl!"

Joe's crap-detector is in perfect condition. It has a converter for Self, but I've never yet seen Joe need it.

Before I forget, this is a conversation I had two days ago with a friend, Nancy Vollmer, age seven:

Me: Nancy, what's more important, having money or getting to like yourself?

The Rotten Years

Nancy: Having money.

Me: What would you do with money?

Nancy: I'd buy myself a mink coat.

Me: A mink coat? What if it was summer?

Nancy: I'd buy myself a summer coat.

Me: But in the summer it's too hot for a coat. And besides, doesn't your mother always buy you clothes?

Nancy: Yes, but I don't like the kind she buys.

Me: Who are you with, most of the time?

Nancy: My mother.

Me: Who are you with at school?

Nancy: My teacher.

Me: Who are you with most when you're asleep?

Nancy: My sister. We sleep in the same bed.

Me: Who are you with when you walk alone from your house to mine?

Nancy: Me, myself and I!

Me: That's right! Don't you see that most of the time, actually all the time, you are with yourself? There is no time that you are away from your own self. So how come you wouldn't want to like yourself?

Nancy: But I like myself.

At this point I ended our conversation. A few minutes after she left my house she called me up to ask what was that question I had asked her. She wanted to try it out on her mother, father, her older sister and older brothers. So you never know. If you spend a lot of time with little kids, they might help you become part of the solution. And if you influence them right, they certainly won't grow up to be part of the problem.

I forgot to give you the results of Mark's and Peter's experiment in trying to make friends with a little kid. Here it is:

Scene: Front yard of a house belonging to the Wallaces, or at least that's what it said on the mailbox. The little Wallace Kid, a second grader (we guessed), is playing out front in the yard.

Mark: Hey, kid, what's more important, doing your homework every night or being kind to somebody every day?

Kid: Doing homework.

Peter: No, it isn't, for God's sake!

Kid: Oh, yeah? It's more important to be, what did you say?

Mark: Kind! Nice to people. You've got to be nice to people every day. It's a lot more important than doing lousy homework.

Peter: Hey, kid, what's more important————

(The door of the kid's house opens and his mother, a mean-looking young broad, appears. She's wearing slacks that are about calf-length and this ratty sweater.)

Kid's mother (*yelling*): What are you doing here?

Mark: Talking to your kid.

Peter: Just talking to your boy, that's all.

Kid's mother (*yelling harder*): Get out of here! Get the hell out of here! Or I'll call the cops.

The Rotten Years

Mark: But lady———

Kid's mother (*yelling like crazy*): Get the hell out! I'm calling the cops.

So we left. The kid's mother must be on a very bad *ego trip*. She probably thought we were selling dope to her seven-year-old. But we're not giving up the assignment.

We think we've found a battered child. We're going to stake out the house every night. If we find out that the kid is being beaten up we're going to go to Chief Woods. It's a real bad scene. The kid (it was over on the other side of town, real slobs) looked like he has bruises all over him. We were talking to him, he's about ten, but the father came out yelling the hell at us, so we beat it. But boy, if they're taking it out on the kid, we're going to do something about it. It's scary out there at night, but what the hell."

"Our experiment is over. Will you stop being troublemakers? There is so much to do and so few willing to do anything. There are thirty-four of you. It's a small army and it's a big war. As time goes on you'll have better ideas than I have today. As your survival of the rotten years continues you'll know that the ego trip you're on is good. For it not only makes you better, but helps everyone around you. I have no right to give you any more assignments, but I can make some suggestions. If you find them good, act on them; if you find better ones, discard mine.

Keep on making friends. With little kids. So many of them are being brainwashed with lies and hate. Because they are so young they believe what they are told. They completely trust their parents. Little kids don't have to scare themselves by the knowledge that they live with and are brought up by people who are often wrong, hateful, and stupid. You can make things right for those kids. You can attend to their education. And you can get your parents to help you. Adults, often, can make sense to each other where children can't.

And what will happen when you help a little kid grow up with love and knowledge of what's important?

(1) You'll be giving the little kid a great thrill (you're a grownup to little kids).
(2) You'll be making sure that the generation right behind you won't be giving you trouble in a few years.
(3) You'll cease to care about what people think of you and begin to care what you think of yourself.

But don't stop with little kids. We simply must do something about orphanages and old people's homes.

When we go into them, it won't be like well-meaning volunteers, but as lovers of those who don't have anyone to love them. Won't you please think of the "Adopt a Friend" idea that Susan had. It's a fine idea, really. The way we can combine it with some *work* is this:

Let's adopt *friends* from among local plumbers, electricians, mechanics, carpenters, and such. There is so little pride in them, in their work, so little integrity, as friends we can find out why that is. Maybe they are unhappy in spite of the money they make, maybe they feel "inferior" because they did not go to college. God, when I think that an auto mechanic who doesn't care can actually be responsible for someone dying in a car accident! We must *care* for them so that they will also care for us.

And daily *"Clean Street Patrols,"* how are they going? We must keep on picking up litter wherever we go and we can say to people who litter: "You look so nice, must you be a litterbug?" or "Did you drop something?" You'll think of much better things to say. And one day we must go and picket the local sanitation department. Those garbage cans are a disgrace. They dirty our streets, and they are a hazard to drivers. How about a sign for them: "You've got a *lousy* job, but we want to be proud of you."

And how about an assembly period for our new friends, the mechanics, carpenters, plumbers, an assembly *discrediting* attending colleges as *not* a necessity of life? If everybody nowadays is expected to go to college, a college degree can't mean the same as it once did. John W. Gardner, the head of Common Cause, wrote in his book *Excellence:* "The society which scorns excellence in plumbing, because plumbing is a humble activity, and tolerates shoddiness in philosophy, because it is an exalted activity, will have neither good plumbing nor good philosophy. Neither its pipes nor its theories will hold water."

And how about going into places of business and trying to determine *how great a toll making money is taking.* Maybe we could find out from some economists if it is feasible to abolish all need for money. I just know it could be done. People could be assured of having all they needed to comfortably live, without having to hate their work, without having to worry very much. Would there be anyone, in a moneyless world, who would be unwilling to help those in need, if he had nothing to lose, neither his time nor his money (since his time would be his own and money would be of no use)? Is there anyone who would object to working only at what he loved? We should make an official-looking questionnaire, and start finding out things we don't know.

You know how I feel about color. I've never found it necessary to divide my students into blacks and whites, but I think the time might have come to do just that. Those of you who are white and who know other whites who hate blacks *must go out and ask why.* And those of you who are black *must go out and find out why* some blacks hate whites. And as you go, destroy the idea that all people are alike, that you can dump them together by race, or color, or what they do, or how much money they have. You know what I found out from my dentist the other day? *Our teeth are as distinct and individual as our fingerprints:* the chances of another person having the same kind of teeth, with the same decay, or fillings, or the number of teeth missing, is so minuscule that probably nobody could find two people with the same mouth!

But you know already that you are unlike anyone else, and that is *our great strength.* We must share that knowledge.

People in this country must have known all this once, before they became so insecure, before they wanted to hide. Before you were born, before your parents came along, before the Depression, there was another breed of Americans who made this country great. They were tough, they *risked* everything, their security, their future, even their lives, for freedom, for their right "to pursue happiness." They did not measure their sacrifices in terms of self-reward or the savings in their banks. But unfortunately, the names you've learned in school, the dates I've been asking you to remember, have little to do with the past from which you came. We must understand the reasons why people were, in many ways, so much better than they are today. For the future's sake we must do that.

So, you see, sitting around, doing nothing but talking on the phone or watching TV is *no longer permissible.* For there is so much to be attended to! And if you must die, and we all must do that, don't let yourself be killed by greed or ignorance or indifference. Don't be caught without having raised a voice in your own defense. For the majority of Americans today is called "the silent majority." And most seem proud to belong there. Have they nothing to say, and are they proud of that? Or have they been silenced, and are they proud of

The Rotten Years

that? *And what had silenced them?* Christ could have lived to a ripe old age, so could have Thomas à Becket, Martin Luther King, John and Bobby Kennedy if they only minded their own business." But their lives would have been wasted.

There are so many alternatives. And so few who take more than one. You don't have to be a "hippie" or a "square," a Wallace lover, Black Panther, Agnew admirer, a radical, a liberal, a militant, or a conservative. Don't let those people on the extremes speak for you! *Don't let me speak for you. Speak for yourselves.* And if you have nothing to say, then ask.

You gave me two assignments: "What are your favorite movies?" and "What are your favorite books?" I made a list of the movies I loved. If they're shown during the weekday on TV, stay home to watch them. If you do, try to make your father stay home from work. It would do both of you a lot of good. And sometime soon we must go around to our local theaters and try to talk the owners into showing some of those great movies.

Whistle Down the Wind	Becket
A Thousand Clowns	A Touch of Evil
Rio Bravo	Cool Hand Luke
Shane	Hud
The Misfits	The Lady Vanishes
The Maltese Falcon	Strangers on a Train
A Face in the Crowd	The Big Sleep
Wuthering Heights	Casablanca
It's a Wonderful Life	To Have and to Have Not
It Happened One Night	Mildred Pierce
The Loneliness of the Long-distance Runner	The Horse's Mouth
The Killers	The Mouse That Roared
Sunset Boulevard	Dead of Night

144

March 27

All movies with W. C. Fields, the Marx Brothers, Greta Garbo, Marlene Dietrich, and John Wayne are musts. If you loved Marilyn Monroe, then all her movies. If you loved Bogart, then see all his movies. And Gable's and Cooper's movies. Any movie with Katherine Hepburn, Spencer Tracy, Jean Arthur, or Margaret Rutherford will be worth your time. You won't have lived fully until you've seen the movies and the people I've mentioned. Since the list is off the top of my head, there are some good ones I've missed. One day theatergoing will be compulsory for kids your age. There are so many great plays. And seeing a play is better for your soul than seeing a movie. All the kids in America should be taken to the Broadway theater. Or maybe Broadway should come to them.

The assignment you gave me on books is much harder than the movie one. It would take me days to get up a good list. But for starters: I wish you wouldn't give up on "children's books." There are some great books published especially for you. A handful that you must read:

> *The Contender* by Robert Lipsyte
> *His Enemy His Friend* by John Tunis
> *Don't Play Dead Before You Have To* by Maia Wojcie-
> chowska
> *A Wrinkle in Time* by Madeleine L'Engle
> *Jazz Country* by Nat Hentoff
> *The Spirit of Jem* by P. M. Newby
> *The Pigman* by Paul Zindel
> *A Season of Ponies* by M. Z. Snyder

And three books that you must read to smaller kids:

> *The Boy Who Could Sing Pictures* by Seymour Leichman
> *The Giving Tree* by Shel Silverstein
> *Where the Wild Things Are* by Maurice Sendak

The Rotten Years

And you *must* read:

> *The Old Man and the Sea* by Ernest Hemingway
> *All the Little Animals* by Walter Hamilton
> *The Castaways* by Jamie Lee Cooper
> *Catcher in the Rye* by J. D. Salinger
> *Slaughterhouse-Five* by Kurt Vonnegut
> *Catch-22* by Joseph Heller

If you haven't read *Wuthering Heights* by Emily Brontë and you're a girl, shame on you!

There are thousands of books. And *you must read,* everything if you don't know which are the good ones. And if you really want to take a *trip,* do it not with acid, but by reading *The Lion, the Witch and the Wardrobe* by C. S. Lewis.

There was a third assignment that you gave me that I'd just as soon forget. "Tell us about sex," you said. I have not much to say about it since I consider the subject very personal. Sex education, if it must exist, should be taught by comedians. And one of you might write the ultimate in sex manuals: *How to be Sexually Happy (365 Days Out of the Year) Without Lifting a Finger.* But there is one great sex book, for both you and your parents, and it's called *The Official Sex Manual* by Gerald Sussman. If you have to read a manual, this is the only one worth bothering with.

When I am not feeling serious about the subject of sex (and I do want to preserve some sanity, sometimes), I make myself believe that we simply *must* go through all that sexual hysteria at this very time. During a moral depression, people want to find out where they've hidden those *inner resources.* So they look in bed. Or take their clothes off in public to see if it would help figure out where they're at.

When I feel serious about it all I can't think of anything but all those young people who are doing their own souls so much harm, and all those children who are destroyed (by abortions or by being unwanted at birth). And I cry.

But you must understand that what you do with sex has nothing to do with what others do with sex.

You have had it very tough. And I don't blame you for being confused, curious, and impatient. What is sex all about? It is not what it seems to be during your rotten years, nor during the *ego trip* that the country is on, nor during our moral depression. (I have a theory, though: the pornographers are the unsung heroes of today. They do more for overpopulation than anyone else, making sex so ridiculous that fewer beginners will be tempted to give it any serious try.)

Your sex life, your personal sex life, is like your soul, your own and neither the well-meaning people nor the pornographers have any business there. Those who are showing you pictures or writing books explaining how you can perform in bed are merely out to make money off sexual retards.

You are born with sex as part of your life, and you die that way. What happens in between cannot be taught to you in school (unless you learn there how you can get to like yourself). If you have sex with someone you are also yourself engaged in sex and if you don't like yourself it will be hard as hell to make love to yourself. But there will be those who will tell you that sex is great—if for nothing more than for clearing up your rotten skin. Others insist that "bad girls" are alive for one reason: to take the burden of your own dislike upon themselves. And others will come up with a thousand reasons why you should not delay but go ahead and try sex during your rotten years, while on your *ego trip*.

The only reason you'll give yourself to another is that you are in love.

But what is love? Does love, by itself, of itself, lead you, through bed, off your *ego trip*?

Too many people think of love as the prize in the box of Cracker Jacks. They are attracted sexually to someone and there it is: love, the cracker-box prize.

There are a hundred different ways you can make yourself believe you are in love. The absence of hate has often been confused with the presence of love. The moment of pleasure has often been taken for love. Love is said to be that which makes you feel good (like food, or sleep or a dress). "I love you," is far, far too easy to say.

You cannot love before you learn how to like. Liking is the first step made toward love. In between that first step and the last, there is a whole world of feelings. So how can you "fall in love at first sight"? Oh, you can!

But what then of sex?

It comes when love is simplified from a four-letter word to three. And it's not "cool" but hot. And any two people feeling that have a right to want or not to want a child. It is not a cracker-box prize, but lust. Shared by two who lust after life and want to share it together.

Is it worth waiting for? you may ask. You cannot live without having lusted after life in the company of another. What if it never happens to me? you may ask. It will. After the trip. It must. *Because the ego trip does not end otherwise.*

When she finished it was past midnight. And for the first time in over two weeks, there was no call from the woman who wished her dead.

Town's Entire Police Force Indicted

'Who's Going To Protect Us?' They Ask After First Shock

Nixon Gets Tough On Bombers
Asks Death Penalty For Killers.

Vandalism

Gunman Is Slain, Policemen Wounded

Nixon Unlimbers His Plan, And Yet Crime Marches On

MARCH 28

MARCH 28

All that day I didn't mention the parade to her. She was strangely calm and quiet, as if she had given up on something. Late that night I went to the basement and made my own sign. I made a wooden cross and I wrote on it: WANTED: SOMEONE TO CARRY IT FOR ME. She found me there, in the basement, and she smashed it to bits and I could not bear to see her face. I went to my room and locked the door against her hate. I had a dream that night and I was awakened by the sounds of her crying. It was four in the morning and she cried for over and hour and then she was quiet and I went back to sleep but I dreamed no more.

On Saturday, March 28, the evening edition of the *Record* carried the following page-one story:

"POLICE CHIEF EXPLAINS DRUGS FROM CHILDREN'S POINT OF VIEW"
At today's meeting of the Tri-State Commission on Narcotics, Police Chief Harold Woods gave a speech written by students at Mark Twain Junior High School.

"What's happening with kids and drugs today is somewhat like what happens during the eclipse of the sun. Some of those who smoke marijuana see the world in a strange, beautiful light. Everything is the same, except nothing is quite the same. Those who go on to other drugs, especially heroin, live in a world where the eclipse goes on forever. Nothing is right because the sun no longer exists for them.

The Rotten Years

"Not everybody is against marijuana," Chief Woods explained, "and not everybody needs to be. The problem is that it is illegal. And the question should be: 'Is this the right time for anyone to get stoned?' If we realize that we are going through a moral depression, then the answer will have to be no."

The students have interviewed several young marijuana users. One said: "When you smoke grass you see yourself in the mirror of your mind. But it's only a reflection of me. When I understood this I stopped spending bread on grass. But God, I wouldn't want my father to get stoned. He might want to do violence to himself."

Chief Woods told the audience that after reading the students' report, he is convinced that they know far more about drugs than most narcotics agents. The students listed several reasons why children become attracted to drugs stronger than marijuana.

"The only kids who start on grass and go on to harder stuff are: (1) Those who thought smoking grass would be a fantastic experience and were disappointed. (2) Those who realize that a grass high simply reflects the emptiness of their minds and souls but don't know how else to fill the emptiness except with hard drugs. (3) Those whose only desire is to be 'like everybody else.' Instead of being aware that they must face up to being individuals, *unlike anybody else*, they live a lie as part of the group. And to try to escape this lie, they get hooked."

Chief Woods emphasized that some kids just like to get stoned on marijuana, as they would on liquor, for pleasure and relaxation. But he expressed the fear that if marijuana were legalized America might become a "grass wasteland. The Indians could cope with drugs but then we introduced them to liquor and destroyed them. With us it's the other way around. We can cope with alcohol, but drugs could destroy us."

In conclusion Chief Woods said: "Some people argue

March 28

about drug addiction, saying that it is a medical rather than a criminal problem. It is neither. It is a spiritual, a moral problem. And as long as we live in an amoral society, a selfish society, we will have a drug problem. And kids will continue being victims of our moral depression."

That evening Elsie Jones wrote four letters. The first one was in answer to a telegram she received that morning urging that she resign.

March 28, 1970

Dear Superintendent Smith,

In spite of that petition drawn up by the PTA and your advice, I cannot resign. Of course you are free to fire me. I've been fired so many times that I'm probably the oldest teacher without tenure. But to resign would be to cop out, to be scared off.

I know I am far from being "popular" with adults. The funny thing, though, is that in the short space of a month, the students in my experiment have also become unpopular. Together we've learned that during a moral depression even doing good is under suspicion. To respond to our times is considered downright subversive. Most parents seem to wish that their kids, instead of cultivating their inner resources, would watch more TV!

But we must all do what it takes to survive these bad times. We must risk making people uncomfortable. We must expect to be mistrusted and misunderstood. Instead of being praised we should expect to be criticized. There is so much unreasonable, insane fear. And fear is the worst of enemies. Martin Luther King had said: "You can't be truly free unless you stop being afraid of death." I hope I have helped my kids realize that they need not fear, not even death. I hope I've helped them become free. And we shall continue being

The Rotten Years

active in a death-fearing society. And we shall continue being troublemakers.

So I cannot quit.

Peace,

Elsie Jones

P.S. I do hope to see you tomorrow at our Truly Christian Easter Parade. E.J.

March 28, 1970

Dear Carl,

Your project sounds like it might save not only our colleges but speed up considerably the coming of age of man. How fantastic! To assign college student one particular problem in the area of their major until the solution is found! And without the solution—no degree! Wow!

I would like you to represent me, if you're not too busy. I want to "test-case" the law prohibiting hitchhiking. I'm going to get a summons and I intend to plead not guilty in the municipal court. When I appeal to the higher courts, I'll need a lawyer. I am against the law on three grounds.

(1) *Legal:* It's unconstitutional, since it tends to discriminate against those too poor to own a car who must depend on inadequate public transportation. Also, I suspect, out of a moral sense many people will soon not be driving. They will be hitchhiking, hence, breaking the law. (Half my male students have promised me that they will not want a car when they're old enough to drive. I'm working on the other half. The girls all seem to think that cars are not vital in their lives. I myself intend to give away my old Falcon and get back to bicycling.)

(2) *Social:* Because cars account for over 60 percent

of man-made pollution we must find less use for our cars but make such use more effective. I foresee that "courtesy stops" will become commonplace. People with cars will feel morally obligated to pick up those without cars. We should not have to consider them lawbreakers.

(3) Moral: The law prohibiting hitchhiking is in effect saying: "Mistrust a stranger on sight." We have so few opportunities to do good for strangers. This is one act that should not be prevented by law. For it is an act of charity and thoughtfulness.

Besides, the law is rarely enforced against children going to and from school. However, long-haired young men are often picked up by the police for hitchhiking, so this law discriminates on appearances. I've never seen a black child hitching rides, probably because a black child knows how little chance he's got of being picked up. Fighting this unjust law seems important. We must have laws that make sense or else we shall have no respect for law. Certainly there are risks involved in picking up a stranger, but what do we do that requires no risk? Avoiding risks would result in death through boredom. After all, what will be remembered of us is not how we died, but how we lived.

I would like you to change my will. I want to leave everything to Robert and Mary Thompson in trust for the baby they're expecting.

Most of all I wish you luck with your project.

Love to you, your kids and your wife,

Elsie Jones

March 28, 1970

Dear Miss Bach,

I have not been avoiding you. I simply have lacked time to give you that interview for the *Record*. But there is no story in me. The story is about the change that happened with the students in my "experimental" class. I hope you'll write it.

They are no longer seekers, but have become finders. I believe they will be the shapers of tomorrow. Of course they are not alone. They belong to a generation that had been told that they have no future. In that way they are a different breed from you and me. For they have nothing to lose.

They have profited, though, from the generation just ahead of them, the college kids who left them a great legacy: opposition to war and being color-blind. Also they have coined a great phrase: "to blow one's mind."

I will not be around, probably, to see them grow up. But I can imagine what they will be like. They will take pleasure in life, no matter how long they will have to enjoy it. I see them living on this endangered planet without greed or thoughtlessness. I see them as a generation of truly existential men, always in the process of changing, in harmony with nature.

But most important I see them having God in their lives. And His presence in them will shape their every act, thought, and word. I see them thinking, unclouded by fear or material wants. I see them as the first totally free men, with absolute respect for life.

This generation, now in their early teens, will have no fear of death because their fate will include the death of this very planet. They will not consider this world to be their only kingdom.

Why don't you interview some of them, these last Christians, these young Americans?

Sincerely,

Elsie Jones
Mark Twain Junior High School

TO MY 9 A.M. CLASS
A LOVE LETTER

At the beginning of this month I had no illusions about you, yet I had every illusion about you. I saw what you were and I saw what you could be.

At the beginning of this month what did we have in common, you and I? You, whose major victory was won over a bra counter, having finally found a 30 AAA which was not called a training bra? And you, who won yours in a barber chair, having lost only an eighth of an inch of hair?

How did we communicate, you and I? You who wanted to blow your mind with glue, grass, acid, pills, and whose mind was like an empty cereal box where you heard nothing but echoes of snap, crackle, and pop? And you, with your vocabulary of "Wow!" alternating with "Outta sight"—how did we talk? What did we talk about?

Were we citizens of the same land, you who thought your nation born over the weekend called Woodstock. And you, who told me you could not trust anyone over thirty, did we swear allegiance to the same flag?

You and I were so different. I was a miser with my time and what did you do with yours? Between attending to your zits, your clothes, your hair, your grades, your dates, you wasted it in a million dulling ways.

You knew nothing of poetry and yet your memory had no trouble retaining a thousand sponsored words spouted by lady plumbers, peroxide fairies, sudsy knights, loud housewives, their deodorized husbands and children made corrupt with brand names.

How could I have influenced you? How could I have become your friend?

The Rotten Years

I watched you take your walks, leaving a trail of gum wrappers behind. I watched you blind abandoned houses of their eyes. I watched you watch and watch that unblinking eye that is your most constant companion. Now that we have yawned as someone walked on the moon's face, do you still dream, as I did at your age, looking up at the night sky?

Were you going to hear what I wanted to say to you, you whose eyes were deader in church than in class, and deader in class than in a supermarket?

I've lusted after life and only resented death as the end of lust. You remained placid as they legalized a rampage against life, the great genocide of innocents. And I wondered if you were going to protest as other "problems," the old, the poor, the blacks, the infirm, the slow to learn, the incompetent, were going to be solved with equal laws, similar madness? I wondered what you will be like, at my age, at fifty past. What will life be like then? Will you have known what you've paid, with what, how much, for what you got? Will you examine what you've sold and what you've bought? I wondered if there will still be a wilderness somewhere, deer running free, pure water, air, a laughing child, a smiling old man, anyone walking a city street at night unafraid, an honest man? I wondered if there would be love.

I don't wonder about any of that now. Because I know that you are alive and well and the world is in good hands.

You have such a great advantage over me. Your future will be so lovely! And if great waves of despair wash over you, they will wash you clean and won't destroy the world. Don't resent being in your rotten years, at a time like this. You are too young, thank God, to participate, to be asked to take sides in grown-up games that so many now play. The winds of change are blowing across your face but they cannot blow you down. When you come of age nobody will have to get dressed up for a revolution. Nobody will have to call anyone bad names. Nobody will believe that the system, the establishment, one or another race, the left or the right, can be blamed for human misery. No one will confuse freedom with license, democracy with capitalism, violence with improvement, fear with people, conformity with courage. And nobody will be able to bargain with hate. This month, during our experiment, I've heard people who had been for war talk against war. Those voices are growing louder and clearer in spite of the sound of dynamite.

I think your timing was just perfect. At about eighteen you'll be coming of age. And so will man.

He might need a bath, his hair might be long, his pockets might be empty, and his language might be vile, and he might be smoking grass. But suddenly he will be off his *ego trip*, which started some two thousand years ago. And he will know that he has reason to like himself: the evidence will be there that he can be godlike.

And when man comes of age, he will be doing it in our country. Of that I am very sure.

But if it doesn't happen, what then?

You will have to get used to being unpopular and unloved. It might even be dangerous for you just to exist. You will have many rotten hours, rotten days and even weeks. But you will never again have rotten years in your life.

Your enemy will be time, for you'll never have enough of it, doing work that others refuse to do.

And very often, in that place of your soul where it is always 2 A.M., you will wonder "What's the use?"

But when things get very bad you'll realize that it is all part of God's design:

> To everything there is a season, and a time to every purpose under the heaven;

The Rotten Years

A time to be born, and a time to die; a time to plant, and a time to pluck up that which is planted;

A time to kill, and a time to heal; a time to mourn and a time to dance;

A time to cast away stones, and a time to gather stones together; a time to embrace, and a time to refrain from embracing;

A time to get, and a time to lose; a time to keep, a time to cast away;

A time to rend, and a time to sew; a time to keep silence, and a time to speak;

A time to love, and time to hate; a time of war, and a time of peace." (*Ecclesiastes*)

Love, *Elsie*

EASTER SUNDAY, MARCH 29

"TROUBLEMAKER" TEACHER IN CRITICAL CONDITION, VICTIM OF ARSONIST

Mrs. Elsie Jones, a history teacher from Mark Twain Junior High School, is in critical condition at the Good Samaritan Hospital.

Early this morning her house was set on fire by an unknown arsonist. Mrs. Jones suffered what the doctors described as "third degree burns." (The *Record* has learned that Mrs. Jones had recently been plagued by crank and threatening telephone calls. The phone company, at her request, disconnected her phone only yesterday.)

The local police chief, Howard Woods, in an interview, said the arsonist "could be just anyone, but not a kid. I wouldn't be surprised if it was a Godfearing parent of one of her students."

Mrs. Jones had recently engaged her students in a series of what she called "survival exercises." Chief Woods said: "Mrs. Jones was concerned about the state of the world. She was just like John and Bobby Kennedy and Martin Luther King and they too have been killed."

Mrs. Elsie Jones was found this morning, unconscious, outside of her home, by the milkman, and rushed to the hospital. Her house was burned to the ground. It is an isolated part of the town. Her nearest neighbors were unaware of the fire and reported having heard nothing suspicious during the night.

FEBRUARY 1, 1971

Today Robert Thompson came to our class. He's writing a book about Mrs. Jones so he talked with each of us who attended her special class. He told us that he named his child Elsie Jones. It was silly but I could not tell him a thing. The others talked their heads off but all I could say was that I had loved her. There are fresh flowers on her grave every day. We all come, one by one, and alone, to see her there.

Things have changed a lot in the world, it seems to me. There are lots of kids who have given up drugs for God and there is even a rock opera called Jesus Christ, Superstar.

And it's different in school now. The teachers haven't changed much, but all the kids have. A reporter from the Record came and interviewed us. They called us "Jesus freaks" but it's just a label, it's not us. We've divided ourselves into two groups: the Seekers of Problems and the Solvers of Problems. We give ourselves assignments. When we carry them out, we get into trouble with a lot of people. We've drafted a constitution—we didn't really know what to call it. We're against cruelty, thoughtlessness, and greed. We're for proving our love, for ourselves and others. We laugh a lot but we're also real serious. We're always around little kids because we've decided that little kids are our best allies.

We all know one thing for sure: we might have gotten where we are now without Mrs. Jones, but it would have taken us an awful long time.

My mother has not left her room in all those months and I don't think she ever will. The other day she began to talk again, but she speaks like a child. Sometimes I think she believes I'm her mother. I take care of her. I read to her a lot, but I don't know if she understands what she hears. Sometimes I think she does, especially

163

The Rotten Years

*when I read from Martin Luther King. I see a light in her eyes when
I read this passage:*

> I don't know what will happen now. We have got difficult
> days ahead, but it doesn't matter with me because I've been to
> the mountaintop. Like anybody else I would like to live a long
> life. But I'm not concerned with that. I just want to do God's
> will and he has allowed me to go up the mountain. I see the
> promised land. I may not get there with you, but I want you to
> know tonight that we as a people will get to the promised land.
> I am happy tonight that I am not worried about anything. I'm
> not fearing any man. Mine eyes have seen the glory of the coming
> of the Lord.

Bill Price read those words at Elsie Jones's funeral.

*I hope I am doing right in not telling the police what I know
my mother has done. They would take her away. But she is my
mother, and I have to love her. She had no one else to do that for
her. And I think that was her whole trouble. The fact that she had
only been loved by me. It wasn't enough.*

MAIA WOJCIECHOWSKA is one of today's most talked-about writers for young people. In books like her best-selling *Tuned Out*, *A Single Light*, and *Shadow of a Bull* (1965 Newbery Medal winner), she explores basic themes of human dignity, self-respect, and personal courage. When she's not talking or writing about young people, Miss Wojciechowska is usually playing tennis, cooking, skiing, riding her horses, going to movies, and infecting other people with her joy in living. Maia Wojciechowska lives in Oakland, New Jersey, with her daughter.